High School Algebra 2 - Math Skills Mastery Lumos tedBook : Online Assessments and Practice Workbooks

Contributing Author   -   John Eaton
Contributing Author   -   Tammie Rolf
Contributing Author   -   Lauren Inzelbuch
Contributing Author   -   Karen O Brien
Contributing Author   -   Donald Woods
Contributing Author   -   Janese Mott
Contributing Author   -   Paul Spinler
Contributing Author   -   Karen Russell
Contributing Author   -   Larry Russell
Executive Producer   -   Mukunda Krishnaswamy
Designer and Illustrator -   Sowmya R.

ISBN-13: 978-1949855180

Printed in the United States of America

For permissions and additional information contact us

Lumos Information Services, LLC
PO Box 1575, Piscataway, NJ 08855-1575
http://www.LumosLearning.com

Email: support@lumoslearning.com
Tel: (732) 384-0146
Fax: (866) 283-6471

Table of Contents	Page #

Introduction

The Lumos Algebra 2 tedBook is specifically designed to improve student achievement on the end of grade exams.

With over a decade of expertise in developing practice resources for standardized tests, Lumos Learning has designed the most efficient methodology to help students succeed on the Algebra 2 Math exams (See Figure 1).

Lumos Smart Test Prep Methodology provides students Algebra 2 test practice along with an efficient pathway to overcome any standards proficiency gaps.

The process starts with students taking the online diagnostic assessment (Practice Test 1). This online diagnostic test will help assess students' proficiency levels in various standards.

After completion of the diagnostic assessment, students can take note of standards where they are not proficient. This step will help educators in developing a targeted remedial study plan based on a student's proficiency gaps. Once the targeted remedial study plan is in place, students can start practicing the lessons in this workbook that are focused on specific standards.

Lumos Smart Test Prep Methodology

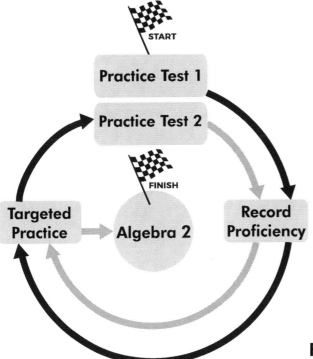

After the student completes the targeted remedial practice, the student should attempt the second online test (Practice Test 2), record the student progress and identify any additional learning gaps after completing the second online test.

Further targeted practice can be planned to help students gain comprehensive skills mastery needed to ensure success in Algebra 2.

Figure 1

Chapter 1
Lumos Smart Test Prep Methodology

Diagnose Learning Gaps and Develop a Study Plan

Step 1: Create your Online Account

Use the URL and access code provided below or scan the QR code to access the first Algebra 2 practice test to get started.

After completing the test, student will receive immediate feedback with detailed reports on standards mastery. With this report, use the next section of the book to design a personalized practice and study plan.

URL	QR Code
Visit the URL below and place the book access code www.lumoslearning.com/a/tedbooks **Access Code: ALG2HS-39042-P**	

Step 2: Complete the Online Algebra 2 Practice Test

Using your Lumos Student Account, please complete the Lumos Algebra 2 test. Please complete the test in a quiet place and follow the instructions provided.

Step 3: Review the Personalized Study Plan Online

After you complete the online practice test, access your individualized study plan from the Table of Contents (Figure 2)

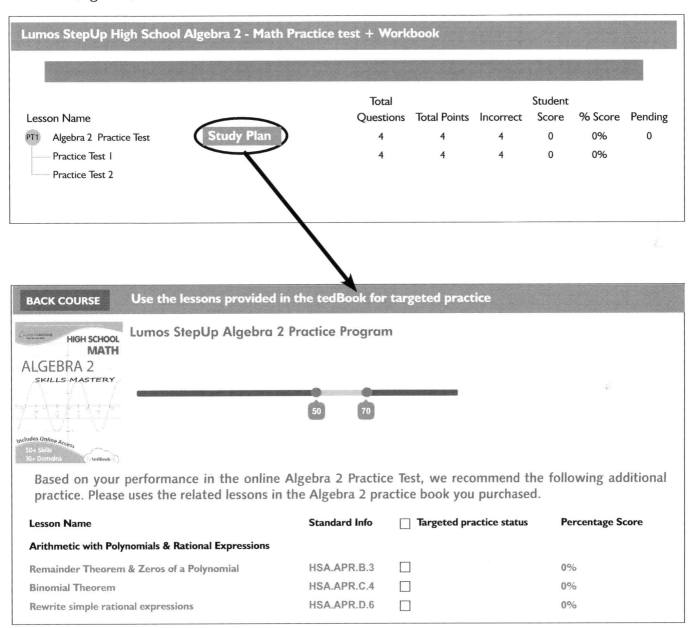

Lumos StepUp High School Algebra 2 - Math Practice test + Workbook							
Lesson Name		Total Questions	Total Points	Incorrect	Student Score	% Score	Pending
PT1 Algebra 2 Practice Test	Study Plan	4	4	4	0	0%	0
Practice Test 1		4	4	4	0	0%	
Practice Test 2							

BACK COURSE   Use the lessons provided in the tedBook for targeted practice

HIGH SCHOOL MATH
ALGEBRA 2
SKILLS MASTERY
Includes Online Access
50+ Skills
10+ Domains

Lumos StepUp Algebra 2 Practice Program

50   70

Based on your performance in the online Algebra 2 Practice Test, we recommend the following additional practice. Please uses the related lessons in the Algebra 2 practice book you purchased.

Lesson Name	Standard Info	Targeted practice status	Percentage Score
Arithmetic with Polynomials & Rational Expressions			
Remainder Theorem & Zeros of a Polynomial	HSA.APR.B.3	☐	0%
Binomial Theorem	HSA.APR.C.4	☐	0%
Rewrite simple rational expressions	HSA.APR.D.6	☐	0%

Figure 2

Step 4: Complete Targeted Practice

Using the information provided in the Study Plan report, complete the Targeted Practice using the appropriate lessons to address proficiency gaps. Using the Lesson Name, find the appropriate practice lessons in this book and answer the questions provided. Please use the answer key and detailed answer explanations provided for each lesson to develop a deeper understanding of the learning objective. (See Figure 3)

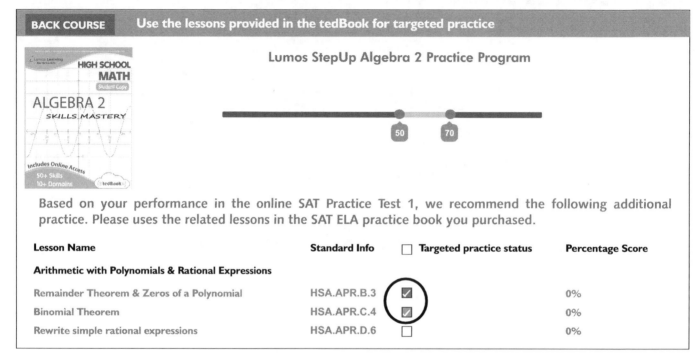

BACK COURSE Use the lessons provided in the tedBook for targeted practice

Lumos StepUp Algebra 2 Practice Program

Based on your performance in the online SAT Practice Test 1, we recommend the following additional practice. Please uses the related lessons in the SAT ELA practice book you purchased.

Lesson Name	Standard Info	Targeted practice status	Percentage Score
Arithmetic with Polynomials & Rational Expressions			
Remainder Theorem & Zeros of a Polynomial	HSA.APR.B.3	☑	0%
Binomial Theorem	HSA.APR.C.4	☑	0%
Rewrite simple rational expressions	HSA.APR.D.6	☐	0%

Figure 3

Step 5: Complete the Online Algebra 2, 2ⁿᵈ Practice Test

After completing the Targeted Practice in the printed book, students should attempt the second Algebra 2 practice test. Please complete the test in a quiet place and follow the instructions provided.

Step 6: Repeat Targeted Practice

Repeat the Targeted Practice by utilizing the lessons provided in this book if additional practice is required.

Visit **www.lumoslearning.com/a/lstp** for more information on **Lumos Smart Test Prep Methodology or Scan the QR Code**

Online Program Benefits

Students*

- Two full-length Lumos Algebra-2 practice tests
- Technology-enhanced item types practice
- Additional learning resources such as videos and apps

Parents*

- You can review your student's online work by login to your parent account
- Pinpoint student areas of difficulty
- Develop custom lessons & assignments

Teachers*

- Review the online work of your students
- Get insightful student reports
- Discover standards aligned videos, apps and books through EdSearch
- Easily access standards information along with the Coherence Map
- Create and share information about your classroom or school events

* Terms and Conditions apply

URL	QR Code
Visit the URL below and place the book access code **www.lumoslearning.com/a/tedbooks** **Access Code: ALG2HS-39042-P**	

Start using the online resources included with this book today!

Discover Engaging and Relevant Learning Resources

Lumos EdSearch is a safe search engine specifically designed for teachers and students. Using EdSearch, you can easily find thousands of standards-aligned learning resources such as questions, videos, lessons, worksheets and apps. Teachers can use EdSearch to create custom resource kits to perfectly match their lesson objective and assign them to one or more students in their classroom.

To access the EdSearch tool, use the search box after you log into Lumos StepUp or use the link provided below.

www.lumoslearning.com/a/edsearchb	

The Lumos Standards Coherence map provides information about previous level, next level and related standards. It helps educators and students visually explore learning standards. It's an effective tool to help students progress through the learning objectives. Teachers can use this tool to develop their own pacing charts and lesson plans. Educators can also use the coherence map to get deep insights into why a student is struggling in a specific learning objective.

Teachers can access the Coherence maps after logging into the StepUp Teacher Portal or use the link provided below.

www.lumoslearning.com/a/coherence-map	

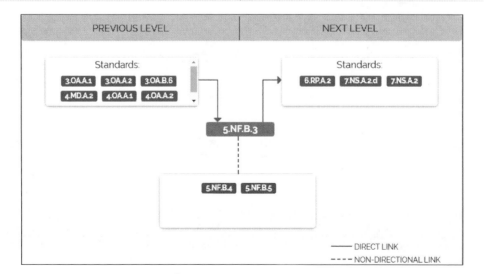

How to use this book effectively

The Lumos Program is a flexible learning tool. It can be adapted to suit a student's skill level and the time available to practice before standardized tests. Here are some tips to help you use this book and the online resources effectively:

Students
- The standards in each book can be practiced in the order designed, or in the order you prefer.
- Complete all problems in each workbook.
- Take the first practice assessment online.
- Have open-ended questions evaluated by a teacher or parent, keeping in mind the scoring rubrics.
- Take the second online practice assessment as you get close to the official test date.
- Complete the test in a quiet place, following the test guidelines. Practice tests provide you an opportunity to improve your test taking skills and to review topics included in the test.

Parents
- Help your child use Lumos StepUp® Online Assessments by following the instructions in "Access Online Program" section.
- You can review your student's online work by login to your parent account.
- You can also conveniently access student progress report on your mobile devices by downloading the Lumos StepUp app. Please follow directions provided in "How can I Download the App?" section in Lumos StepUp® Mobile App FAQ For Parents and Teachers.

Test Taking Tips

1) **The day before the test,** make sure you get a good night's sleep.

2) **On the day of the test,** be sure to eat a good hearty breakfast! Also, be sure to arrive at school on time.

3) **During the test:**
- **Read every question carefully.**

  - Do not spend too much time on any one question. Work steadily through all questions in the section.
  - Attempt all of the questions even if you are not sure of some answers.
  - If you run into a difficult question, eliminate as many choices as you can and then pick the best one from the remaining choices. Intelligent guessing will help you increase your score.
  - Also, mark the question so that if you have extra time, you can return to it after you reach the end of the section.
  - Some questions may refer to a graph, chart, or other kind of picture. Carefully review the infographics before answering the question.
  - Be sure to include explanations for your written responses and show all work.

- **While Answering TECR questions.**
  - Read the directions of each question. Some might ask you to drag something, others to select, and still others to highlight. Follow all instructions of the question (or questions if it is in multiple parts)

Workbook
Chapter 2

Algebra

1. Evaluate the function $f(x) = 3x^3 - 3x^2 + 2x + 14$ at $x = 2$ using the Remainder Theorem, with synthetic division.

   Ⓐ -26
   Ⓑ 30
   Ⓒ 26
   Ⓓ -30

2. You are showing that you can evaluate a function using the Remainder Theorem. You state that you can evaluate g(-4) for $g(x) = 2x^2 - 5x - 3$ by dividing the function by $x + 4$, using synthetic division. What is g (-4)?

   Ⓐ 49
   Ⓑ 9
   Ⓒ 39
   Ⓓ -49

3. Evaluate the function $h(x) = (x^4 + x^3 - 3x^2 - 4x - 5)$ at x=2 using the Remainder Theorem, with synthetic division.

   Ⓐ 1
   Ⓑ 34
   Ⓒ -1
   Ⓓ -34

4. Find the remainder when $2x^3 - 5x + x - 3$ is divided by x -1.

   Ⓐ -3
   Ⓑ there is no remainder
   Ⓒ -11
   Ⓓ -5

5. Evaluate $f(a) = -a^3 + 6a - 7$ at a = -1 and state the remainder.

   Ⓐ -14
   Ⓑ -12
   Ⓒ 14
   Ⓓ 12

6. **What are the zeros of h(x) = (x² + 4x - 12).**

    Ⓐ 6, 2
    Ⓑ -6, 2
    Ⓒ -6, -2
    Ⓓ 6, -2

7. **What are the zeros of f(x) = (x³ + 16x² + 64x).**

    Ⓐ 0, 16
    Ⓑ -8, 0
    Ⓒ -4, 0
    Ⓓ 0, 8

8. **What are the zeros of g(x) = x² + 11x + 18.**

    Ⓐ 9, 2
    Ⓑ -9, 2
    Ⓒ 9, -2
    Ⓓ -9, -2

9. **What are the zeros of f(x) = x² + x - 90.**

    Ⓐ -10, 9
    Ⓑ 10, 9
    Ⓒ 10, -9
    Ⓓ -10, -9

10. **What are the zeros of h(x) = (x² - 13x + 40).**

    Ⓐ -5, 8
    Ⓑ 5, 8
    Ⓒ -8, 5
    Ⓓ -8, -5

Lesson 2: Binomial Theorem

1. Use the binomial theorem to expand $(2x-y)^3$

   What is the second term in the binomial expansion?

   Ⓐ $-12xy^2$
   Ⓑ $-12x^2y$
   Ⓒ $12x^2y$
   Ⓓ $12xy^2$

2. Use the binomial theorem to expand $(x+5)^5$

   What is the fourth term in the binomial expansion?

   Ⓐ $625x^2$
   Ⓑ $1250x^3$
   Ⓒ $1250x^2$
   Ⓓ $25x^4$

3. Use the binomial theorem to expand $(2x^3+1)^4$

   What is the third term in the binomial expansion?

   Ⓐ $24x^3$
   Ⓑ $48x^2$
   Ⓒ $24x^6$
   Ⓓ $6x^6$

4. Use the binomial theorem to expand $(x+1)^6$

   What will be the value of 6th term. Write the correct answer choice into the box below.

   Ⓐ $6x^2$
   Ⓑ $6x$
   Ⓒ $20x^3$
   Ⓓ $15x^2$

5. Use the binomial theorem to expand $(3x-1)^5$

   What is the fourth term in the binomial expansion?

   Ⓐ $90x^2$
   Ⓑ $-90x^2$
   Ⓒ $-90x^3$
   Ⓓ $90x^3$

Lesson 3: Rewrite Simple Rational Expressions

1. **Rewrite the rational expression below in simplified form.**

$$\frac{x+(x-y)^2-y}{(x-y)^3}$$

Ⓐ $\dfrac{1}{(x-y)^2} - \dfrac{1}{x-y}$

Ⓑ $\dfrac{1}{(x-y)^2} + \dfrac{1}{x-y}$

Ⓒ $\dfrac{2(x+y)}{(x-y)^2}$

Ⓓ $\dfrac{2}{(x-y}$

2. **Rewrite the rational expression below in simplified form.**

$$\frac{3x^3+5x^2-7}{x^3}$$

Ⓐ $\dfrac{3}{x^2} + \dfrac{5}{x} - \dfrac{7}{x^3}$

Ⓑ $3 - \dfrac{5}{x} - \dfrac{7}{x^3}$

Ⓒ $3 + \dfrac{5}{x} - \dfrac{7}{x^3}$

Ⓓ $\dfrac{5}{x} - \dfrac{4}{x^3}$

3. **Rewrite the rational expression below in simplified form.**

$$\frac{5x^2+6x-2}{2x^2}$$

Ⓐ $5 + \dfrac{3}{x} - \dfrac{1}{x^2}$

Ⓑ $\dfrac{5}{2} + \dfrac{3}{x} - \dfrac{1}{x^2}$

Ⓒ $\dfrac{5}{2} - \dfrac{3}{x} - \dfrac{1}{x^2}$

Ⓓ $\dfrac{5}{2} + \dfrac{3}{x^2} - \dfrac{1}{x}$

4. **Rewrite the rational expression below in simplified form.**

$$\frac{7(x+4) - 3(x+4)^3}{(x+4)^2}$$

   Ⓐ $\dfrac{7}{x+4} - 3$

   Ⓑ $\dfrac{7}{x+4} - 3(x+4)$

   Ⓒ $\dfrac{7}{x+4} + 3(x+4)$

   Ⓓ $\dfrac{3}{x+4} - 7(x+4)$

5. **Rewrite the rational expression below in simplified form.**

$$\frac{9x^3 - 12x^2 + 15x}{3x^3}$$

   Ⓐ $3 + \dfrac{4}{x} - \dfrac{5}{x^2}$

   Ⓑ $3 - \dfrac{4}{x} + \dfrac{5}{x^2}$

   Ⓒ $3 + \dfrac{4}{x} - \dfrac{5}{x^3}$

   Ⓓ $3 - \dfrac{5}{x} + \dfrac{4}{x^2}$

1. Simeon is two years older than Brina. The product of their ages is 63. If *b*, represents Brina's age, which equation below can be used to find Simeon's age?

   (A) b(b + 2) = 63
   (B) s+b+2 = 63
   (C) s(b+2) = 63
   (D) None of these

2. The Thomas Company is planning to increase the area of their warehouse by 30%. The rectangular space currently measures 200 by 500 feet. If they want to increase the length and width by the same amount, *x*, which equation will represent the area of their new warehouse?

   (A) (200 * 500)x + .20 = 130,000
   (B) (200 + x)(500 + x) = 130,000
   (C) (200 + x)(500 + x) = 100,000
   (D) (200 + 500)x = 100,000

3. Tuition plus Room and Board (TRB) at Truman University for freshman year is $150,000 a year. If it increases by 5% each year, what will TRB cost four years later, for senior year, rounded to the nearest dollar?

   (A) $182,326
   (B) $180,000
   (C) $157,500
   (D) $630,000

4. Thomas wants to make at least $2,000 over winter break between semesters. Amazon is hiring for holiday delivery persons at a rate of $29.95 per hour. How many hours will Thomas need to work to meet his goal? Write your answer in the below box.

5. Sadie was sent to the store to buy boxes of cake mix for a party. Her mother was a math teacher so she made a math problem out of her shopping trip. She told Sadie that 5 boxes of cake mix cost $20.50. She sent her to the store to buy 7 boxes of cake mix. Sadie took $30 with her to the store. Does she have enough money? Yes, or no -- justify your answer.

Lesson 5: Explaining Equation and Using Properties

1. **What is the solution to 8x-8=96?**

   Ⓐ 19
   Ⓑ 13
   Ⓒ -13
   Ⓓ -19

2. **What is the solution to 6x+5=101?**

   Ⓐ 19
   Ⓑ 13
   Ⓒ 17
   Ⓓ 16

3. **What is the solution to $\dfrac{x}{5}$ - 7=23? Write the correct answer choice into the box below.**

   Ⓐ 80
   Ⓑ 150
   Ⓒ -196
   Ⓓ 196

4. **What is the solution to $\dfrac{x}{3}$ +46=61? Select the correct answer choice.**

   Ⓐ 321
   Ⓑ 37
   Ⓒ 45
   Ⓓ -19

5. **What is the solution to $\dfrac{x}{3}$ + 5=17? Enter your answer as an integer.**

Lesson 6: Solve Linear Equations And Inequalities With One Variable

1. Solve for x:

   2x - 4 = 10.

   Ⓐ 3
   Ⓑ 14
   Ⓒ 7
   Ⓓ -7

2. Solve for y:

   $72 = \dfrac{y}{3}$

   Ⓐ 24
   Ⓑ 216
   Ⓒ 69
   Ⓓ 75

3. What is the value of x in the equation 5(2x - 7)=15x - 10?

   Ⓐ 1
   Ⓑ 0.6
   Ⓒ -5
   Ⓓ -9

4. Which value of x is in the solution set for the inequality: 2x - 5 > x - 2

   Ⓐ -4
   Ⓑ 12
   Ⓒ -6
   Ⓓ -8

5. In the set of positive integers, what is the solution set of the inequality 2x - 3 < 5?

   Ⓐ {0,1,2,3}
   Ⓑ {1,2,3}
   Ⓒ {0,1,2,3,4}
   Ⓓ {1,2,3,4}

1. **What are the solutions to the quadratic equation below?**

   $2x^2 + 8x + 6 = 0$

   Ⓐ -1, 3
   Ⓑ 1, 3
   Ⓒ 1, -3
   Ⓓ -1, -3

2. **What are the solutions to the quadratic equation below?**

   $4x^2 + 8x + 4 = 0$

   Ⓐ 1
   Ⓑ -2, 1
   Ⓒ -1
   Ⓓ -2, -1

3. **Solve the quadratic equation $2x^2 + 9x - 5 = 0$.**

   Ⓐ 5, -9
   Ⓑ $\dfrac{1}{2}$, -5
   Ⓒ $\dfrac{-1}{2}$, 5
   Ⓓ -5, 9

4. **Solve the equation $x^2 - 9x + 20 = 0$.**

   Ⓐ 4, 5
   Ⓑ - 4, - 5
   Ⓒ 9, - 20
   Ⓓ - 9, 20

5. **Solve the quadratic $-8p^2 = 40p$.**

   Ⓐ 0, - 5
   Ⓑ 0, 5
   Ⓒ - 8, 40
   Ⓓ 8, - 40

Lesson 8: Solving Systems of Equations in Two Variables

1. Use the elimination method to solve the system of equations.

$$\begin{cases} 5x+2y=0 \\ 3x-2y=-16 \end{cases}$$

Ⓐ (-5, 2)
Ⓑ (2, -5)
Ⓒ (-2, 5)
Ⓓ (5, -2)

2. What is the solution to the system

$$\begin{cases} -2x=y-1 \\ y+x=4 \end{cases}$$

Ⓐ (2, -4)
Ⓑ (7, -3)
Ⓒ
Ⓓ (-3, 7)

3. Solve the system of equations below by replacing one equation with the sum of the two equations or by a multiple of the equation, and then adding the two equations together. Write the correct answer choice into the box below.

$4x-3y=6$

$2x-5y=-4$

Ⓐ (3,2)
Ⓑ (5,4)
Ⓒ (2,3)
Ⓓ (3,1)

4. Solve the system of equations below by replacing one equation with the sum of the two equations or by a multiple of the equation, and then adding the two equations together.
$4x+5y=3$
$3x+2y=4$

1. A company ordered two types of parts, copper and steel. A shipment containing 2 copper and 3 steel parts costs $26. A second shipment containing 1 copper and 5 steel parts costs $27. Find the cost of a copper part.

2. Shelly set up a system of equations to solve the following problem. What is wrong with her setup? What are the correct equations?

   A music store receives shipments of keyboards and guitars. A shipment of 10 keyboards and 5 guitars costs $600. A shipment of 2 keyboards and 8 guitars costs $470. Find the cost of a keyboard and the cost of a guitar.

   $$\begin{cases} 5k+10g=600 \\ 2k+8g=470 \end{cases}$$

3. Write the matrix with the correct values from a system of equations that could be used to solve the following problem using the matrix method.

   Janet wants to buy pets for each of her ten grandchildren for Easter. If she buys 2 bunny rabbits and 8 goldfish, she will spend $64. If she buys 5 bunny rabbits and 5 goldfish, she will spend $85. Find the cost of a bunny rabbit and the cost of a goldfish.

4. Two numbers have a sum of 24 and a difference of 6. Write a linear system of equations and solve to find the two numbers.

    Ⓐ 10, 14
    Ⓑ 15, 9
    Ⓒ No solution
    Ⓓ 19, 5

5. Solve the system of equations by graphing the lines.

    $3x+y=4$

    $3x-y=2$

    Ⓐ (1,0)
    Ⓑ (1,2)
    Ⓒ (1,1)
    Ⓓ (2,1)

1. At what point, in the first quadrant, do the two functions $f(x)=x^2+8x-15$ and $g(x)=-x^2+4x+15$ intersect?

   Ⓐ (3,18)
   Ⓑ (−5,−30)
   Ⓒ (18,3)
   Ⓓ (−30,−5)

2. At what point, in the first quadrant, do the two functions $f(x)=3x^2-9x-6$ and $g(x)=2x^2-6x+4$ intersect?

   Ⓐ (−2,24)
   Ⓑ (5,30)
   Ⓒ (3,17)
   Ⓓ (5,24)

3. At what point, that is closest to (0,0) do the two functions $f(x)=5x^2+25x+60$ and $g(x)=4x^2+6x$ intersect?

   Ⓐ (−2,30)
   Ⓑ (−4,40)
   Ⓒ (−3,30)
   Ⓓ (−5,60)

4. At what point, that is closest to (0,0) do the two functions $f(x)=2x^2-7x+39$ and $g(x)=x^2+7x-1$ intersect?

   Ⓐ (10,169)
   Ⓑ (2,33)
   Ⓒ (4,43)
   Ⓓ (3,36)

5. When you locate a point on the graph that you believe to be the intersection, what is the best way to check your answer?

   Ⓐ Plug the x-value of the believed intersection point into both equations and solve for y to see if the y-values match for both equations.
   Ⓑ Plug the x-value of the believed intersection point into one equation and solve for y to see if the y-value matches
   Ⓒ Plug in the y-value of the believed intersection point into one equation and solve for x to see if the x-value matches
   Ⓓ You don't need to check, you are probably right

Lesson 11: Solve Simple Rational and Radical Equations in One Variable

1. What is the solution to the radical equation $\sqrt{x} = 0.9$?

   Ⓐ 0.3
   Ⓑ 0.81
   Ⓒ 0.18
   Ⓓ 1.8

2. What is the solution to the radical equation $\sqrt{4x-3} = \sqrt{5x}$?

   Ⓐ -3
   Ⓑ Infinitely many solutions
   Ⓒ 3
   Ⓓ No real solution

3. What is the solution to the rational equation $\dfrac{2}{x+6} = \dfrac{-6}{x-4}$?

   Ⓐ $\dfrac{7}{2}$

   Ⓑ $-\dfrac{2}{7}$

   Ⓒ $\dfrac{2}{7}$

   Ⓓ $-\dfrac{7}{2}$

4. What is the solution to the radical equation $\sqrt{x} = 0.36$?

   Ⓐ 0.6
   Ⓑ 0.06
   Ⓒ 0.1296
   Ⓓ 0.72

5. What is the solution to the radical equation $\sqrt{9y-5} = \sqrt{7y}$?

   Ⓐ $\dfrac{5}{2}$

   Ⓑ Infinitely many solutions

   Ⓒ $-\dfrac{7}{2}$

   Ⓓ

Lesson 12: Solve a Simple System Consisting of a Linear Equation and a Quadratic Equation

1. Solve this system of equations algebraically.

   $$y=2$$
   $$x^2+y^2=16$$

   Ⓐ $(2\sqrt{3},-2)$
   Ⓑ $(-2\sqrt{3},-2)$
   Ⓒ $(\pm2\sqrt{3},-2)$
   Ⓓ $(\pm12,-2)$

2. Solve this system of equations algebraically.

   $$x = 2$$
   $$x^2+y^2=25$$

   Ⓐ $(\pm\sqrt{21},2)$
   Ⓑ $(2,\pm\sqrt{21})$
   Ⓒ $(2,\sqrt{21})$
   Ⓓ $(2,-\sqrt{21})$

3. Based on the graph, how many solutions would there be for a system of equations that included only the circle and parabola function pictured?

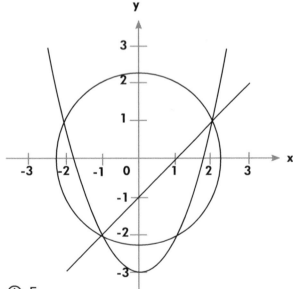

   Ⓐ Four
   Ⓑ Two
   Ⓒ Three
   Ⓓ One

4. **What are the points of intersection for the system of equations** $y = 4x^2 - 4$ **and** $y = 3x$**?**

Ⓐ (4.32, 1.44) and (-69, -2.07)
Ⓑ (4.32, 1.44) and (-2.07, -.69)
Ⓒ No solution
Ⓓ (1.44, 4.32) and (-.69, -2.07)

5. **What are the points of intersection for the system of equations?**

$y = -5x^2 + 3$ **and** $y = 2x + 5$**?**

Ⓐ (0, 0)
Ⓑ (-1, -1)
Ⓒ
Ⓓ (0, 3)

1. What is a numerical factor of the expression $36x^2+12x+24$?

   Ⓐ x
   Ⓑ 12
   Ⓒ 24
   Ⓓ 12x

2. What is the numerical coefficient of the third term the expression $5x^3y^4 + 7x^2y^3 - 6xy^2 - 8xy$?

   Ⓐ 6
   Ⓑ 7
   Ⓒ -8
   Ⓓ -6

3. The formula $P(1+r)^t$ is used to calculate the amount in an account that earns interest compounded annually, where, P is the principal in the account, r is the annual interest rate (as a decimal) and t is the time (in years). What is the interest rate in the expression $500(1.025)^7$?

   Ⓐ 1.5%
   Ⓑ 2.5%
   Ⓒ 1.025%
   Ⓓ 25%

4. The formula $P(1+r)^t$ is used to calculate the amount in an account that earns interest compounded annually, where, P is the principal in the account, r is the annual interest rate (as a decimal) and t is the time (in years). If the expression $1500(1.0355)^9$ was used to calculate the amount of money in an account, how many years was the money in the account?

   Ⓐ 1500
   Ⓑ 3.55
   Ⓒ 9
   Ⓓ 1.0355

5. What is the numeric coefficient of the third term in the expression $12a^3b^2c^6 + 7abc - 5a^2bc$? Highlight by circling the correct answer choice.

   Ⓐ 7
   Ⓑ 5
   Ⓒ -5
   Ⓓ 12

1. Which expression is equivalent to $6y^2 - 3xy + 5yx + 13y^2$?

   Ⓐ $6y^2 + 2xy + 13y^2$
   Ⓑ $6y^2 + 8xy + 13y^2$
   Ⓒ $6y^2 - 8xy + 13y^2$
   Ⓓ $6y^2 - 2xy + 13y^2$

2. Factor completely $9ab^2 - 6ab - 3a$

3. Scott factored $\tan^3 x - 16\tan x$ into $\tan x^3(\tan x + 4)(\tan x - 4)$. Did he do it correctly? Explain your answer.

4. In the table below, check off any columns that show a factor of the expression given in the table:

	d + 6	d - 6	d + 2	d - 2	d + 4
$d^4 - 4d^2 + 8d^3 - 32d + 12d^2 - 48$	☐	☐	☐	☐	☐

5. State whether the following statement in the table below is true or false.

	True	False
The expression 3x + 5y is a prime polynomial because it's coefficients are prime numbers.	○	○

Lesson 15: Writing Expressions In Equivalent Forms

1. **Which is the solution set of the equation $(x-3)(x+2)=0$?**

   Ⓐ 3 and - 2
   Ⓑ 3 and 2
   Ⓒ - 3 and 2
   Ⓓ - 3 and - 2

2. **Which step can be used when solving $x^2-6x-16=0$, by completing the square?**

   Ⓐ $x^2-6x-9=16-9$
   Ⓑ $x^2-6x+36=16+36$
   Ⓒ $x^2-6x+9=16+9$
   Ⓓ $x^2-6x-36=-36+9$

3. **Which expression is equivalent to $9x^2-25y^2$:**

   Ⓐ $(3x-5y)^2$
   Ⓑ $(3x+5y)^2$
   Ⓒ $(3x^2-5y)(3x^2+5y)$
   Ⓓ $(3x+5y)(3x-5y)$

4. **The value of Tom's 45-foot catamaran depreciates at a rate of 18% per year. The boat cost Tom \$150,000. What equation will show the depreciation of the boat's value after *t* years if *V* represents the value?**

   Ⓐ $V=150,000(.82)^t$
   Ⓑ $V=150,000(.18)^t$
   Ⓒ $V=150,000(.82)^{\frac{t}{12}}$
   Ⓓ $V=150,000(1.82)^t$

5. **A study of fish in a man-made lake in Florida showed there was a population decrease of 25% over a decade. The model used to was $P=420(.75)^d$, where *d* is the decades after 2010, and *P* is the population in thousands. A new study would like to predict the population after *y* years. Which equation below can be used for the prediction?**

   Ⓐ $P=420(.0563)^y$
   Ⓑ $P=420(.9716)^y$
   Ⓒ $P=420(.9750)^y$
   Ⓓ $P=420(.6501)^y$

1. Write a formula to describe the sum of the finite geometric series if $a_1=3$, $r=2$. Use your formula to find the sum of the first 6 terms in the series.

   Ⓐ -189
   Ⓑ 96
   Ⓒ 189
   Ⓓ -96

2. Write a formula to describe the sum of the finite geometric series if the first three terms are -6, -30, -150... . Use your formula to find the sum of the first 8 terms in the series.

   Ⓐ -585,934.5
   Ⓑ -585,936
   Ⓒ -2,343,744
   Ⓓ 585,936

3. Write a formula to describe the sum of the finite geometric series if $a_1=-6$, $r=-3$. Use your formula to find the sum of the first 10 terms in the series.

   Ⓐ -88,572
   Ⓑ -14,762.25
   Ⓒ 14,762.25
   Ⓓ 88,572

4. Write a formula to describe the sum of the finite geometric series if the first three terms are 2+6+18... . Use your formula to find the sum of the first 12 terms in the series.

   Ⓐ 531,440
   Ⓑ 177,146
   Ⓒ 59,048
   Ⓓ 1,594,322

5. Find the sum of the series $\sum_{i=1}^{10} 3(-2)^{i-1}$

   Ⓐ 1023
   Ⓑ -1023
   Ⓒ 2046
   Ⓓ None of these

End of Algebra

Workbook
Chapter 3

Functions

Lesson 1: Writing Functions that Describe a Relationship Between Two Quantities

1. **Which of the following is an expression with a degree of 7, leading coefficient of 2 and a constant of negative 8.**

   Ⓐ $-8x^7 - x^2 - 2$
   Ⓑ $2x^5 - x^2 - 8$
   Ⓒ $2x^7 - x^2 - 8$
   Ⓓ $-8x^5 - x^2 - 2$

2. **Thomas bought a baseball bat and two gloves for a total of d dollars. If g represents the cost of one glove, what expression represents the cost of the baseball bat?**

   Ⓐ $d + 2g$
   Ⓑ $2g - d$
   Ⓒ $d - 2g$
   Ⓓ $d + \dfrac{9}{2}$

3. **If x -7 is an even integer, what is the next consecutive even integer?**

   Ⓐ $x - 3$
   Ⓑ $x - 5$
   Ⓒ $x + 9$
   Ⓓ $x - 9$

4. **What expression represents the number of inches in x feet?**

   Ⓐ $\dfrac{x}{12}$
   Ⓑ $12x$
   Ⓒ $\dfrac{12}{x}$
   Ⓓ $x - 9$

5. **The perimeter of an equilateral triangle with side length x + 5 is:**

   Ⓐ $(x + 5) + (x + 5) + (x + 5)$
   Ⓑ $3(x + 5)$
   Ⓒ $3x + 15$
   Ⓓ All of these

1. If a ball rolls down a hill and falls 4ft in the first second, 8ft in the next second, and 16ft in the third, How far will it fall in the 8th second?

2. Jonathan wrote an explicit and recursive equation to represent the sequence 2, 4, 8, ... as f(n)=2n but he is wrong. Tell why he is wrong and write the correct equation to represent this sequence.

3. Fill in the table with the 30th number in the sequence.

Term #	Terms in sequence
1	1
2	6
3	11
4	16
30	

4. Your allowance increases by $2.50 every year and you start at $10 the first year. Which could represent your allowance as a function of years.

    Ⓐ $F(n) = 10.00 + 2.50n$
    Ⓑ $F(n) = 7.50 + 2.50n$
    Ⓒ $F(n) = 7.50n + 2.50$
    Ⓓ $F(n) = 10.00n + 2.50$

5. If the explicit function that represents your phone bill is $P(y) = 100 \times 1.03^{y-1}$ after y years, what would be an equivalent recursive function?

    Ⓐ $P(y-1) = P(y) \times 1.03$, where $P(1) = 100$
    Ⓑ $P(y) = P(y-1) \times 1.03^{y}$, where $P(1) = 100$
    Ⓒ $P(y) = P(y-1) \times 1.03^{y-1}$, where $P(1) = 100$
    Ⓓ $P(y) = P(y-1) \times 1.03$, where $P(1) = 100$

1. **Describe the function $f(x) = 2x$ as either even or odd.**

   [ ]

2. **Fill in the table below with the correct values to show the transformation of $f(x) = x$ to $g(x) = x + 3$.**

x	f(x)	g(x)
0		
1		
-1		
8		

3. **Match each x-value with the correct y-value that would show the transformation of $f(x) = x^2$ to $g(x) = -2x^2$**

f(x)	g(x)
0	-2
4	-8
¼	0
1	-½

4. **If $f(x) = x^2$ and $g(x) = 3x^2$, what is the amount of vertical stretch when converting from $f(x)$ to $g(x)$?.**

   [ ]

5. **Describe the difference between $y_1 = 3x$ and $y_2 = 3x - 7$.**

   [ ]

Lesson 4: Finding Inverse Functions

1. Find $f^{-1}(x)$ when $f(x)=7x-1$

    Ⓐ $7x+1$
    Ⓑ $-7x+1$
    Ⓒ $\dfrac{x+1}{7}$
    Ⓓ $\dfrac{x-1}{7}$

2. What is the inverse function of $f(x)=\sqrt{3x}-2$?

    Ⓐ $f^{-1}(x)=\dfrac{(x-2)^2}{-3}$
    Ⓑ $f^{-1}(x)=\dfrac{(x-2)^2}{3}$
    Ⓒ $f^{-1}(x)=\dfrac{(x+2)^2}{3}$
    Ⓓ $f^{-1}(x)=\dfrac{(x+2)^2}{-3}$

3. What is the inverse of the function $f(x)=3^x$?

    Ⓐ $f^{-1}(x)=\log_3 x$
    Ⓑ $f^{-1}(x)=\log x$
    Ⓒ $f^{-1}(x)=x^2$
    Ⓓ Inverse does not exist

4. A linear function has the points (-1, 4), (2, 7), and (5, 10). Which of the following points will the inverse have?

    Ⓐ (0, 6)
    Ⓑ (4, -2)
    Ⓒ (10, 3)
    Ⓓ (7, 2)

5. In order to make $f(x)=x^2$ an invertible function, its domain should be which of the following?

    Ⓐ $x\geq0$
    Ⓑ $x\leq0$
    Ⓒ $x\neq0$
    Ⓓ $x\in R$

Lesson 5: Recognizing that Sequences are Functions

1. **What is the recursive formula for this arithmetic sequence? 5,19,33,47,...**

    A $a_n = a_{n-1} + 14$
    B $a_n = a_{n-1} \times 14$
    C $a_n = a_{n-1} + 5$
    D $a_n = 14 + 5(n-1)$

2. **What is the recursive formula for this geometric sequence? 3,18,108,648,...**

    A $a_n = a_{n-1} \times 6$
    B $a_n = a_1 \times 6^{n-1}$
    C $a_n = a_{n-1} \times -6$
    D $a_n = a_{n-1} \times (6)^n$

3. **What is the recursive formula for this geometric sequence? 2, -8, 32, -128,...**

    A $a_n = a_{n-1} \times -4$
    B $a_n = a_1 \times (-4)^{n-1}$
    C $a_n = a_{n-1} \times 4$
    D $a_n = a_{n-1} \times (-4)^n$

4. **What is the formula for this sequence 1,2,2,4,8,32,256... in the domain n>2?**

    A $a_n = a_{n-2} \times a_n$
    B $a_n = a_{n+1} \times a_{n-1}$
    C $a_n = a_{n-2} \times a_{n-1}$
    D $a_n = a_{n-3} \times a_{n-2}$

5. **What is the 9th number of the Fibonacci sequence that starts as follows (1, 1, 2, 3, 5, 8, 13.....)?**

Lesson 6: Modeling Functional Relationships with Tables and Graphs

1. The information in the table shows the how many new customer applications are processed each hour by the company's call center. The company has a goal of processing 10 new customers per hour. During which hour does the call center meet the company's goal?

Hour	New Customers Processed
1	9
2	7
3	6
4	11
5	8

Ⓐ 4
Ⓑ 1
Ⓒ 1 and 4
Ⓓ 5

2. An air conditioning company repairs air conditioning units 24-hours per day. The table below shows the customer complaints and compliments about repair technicians. Based on the data in the table, which shift appears to be doing the best job?

Time	Complaints	Compliments
Midnight to 6 am	3	2
6 am to Noon	6	9
Noon to 6pm	4	12
6pm to Midnight	8	7

Ⓐ Midnight to 6am
Ⓑ 6am to Noon
Ⓒ Noon to 6pm
Ⓓ 6pm to Midnight

3. The table below shows the arrivals and departures from an all-day college football passing contest. During which two-hour period are the most people at the contest?

Time	Arriving per Hour	Departing per Hour
8:00-10:00	260	80
10:00-12:00	175	90
12:00-2:00	160	100
2:00-4:00	120	150
4:00-6:00	90	195
6:00-8:00	20	210

Ⓐ 2:00pm - 4:00pm
Ⓑ 10:00am - 12:00pm
Ⓒ 12:00pm - 2:00pm
Ⓓ 8:00am - 10:00am

4. The table below shows the results of testing whether drill press operators are meeting the accuracy standards of drilling holes the correct depth. The specification for depth is 16mm ± 0.3mm. The company awards five points for every 100 holes whose depths are within the specification and subtracts one point for each hole that is not within specification. Sam drilled the most holes that were not within specifications. How many points will he receive?

Operator	#Within Specs	#Not within Specs
Joe	1300	6
Pete	1500	5
Dave	1300	8
Sam	1900	11

5. Which of the following is an equation of a parabola with x-intercepts at (-2, 0) and (-3, 0) and a y-intercept at (0, 6)?

Ⓐ $y=x^2-5x+6$
Ⓑ $y=x^2+5x-6$
Ⓒ $y=x^2+5x+6$
Ⓓ $y=x^2-5x-6$

1. **If it rains 3 inches on Tuesday and increases to 10 inches by Friday, what rate of increase in inches per day?**

    Ⓐ $2\frac{1}{3}$ inches per day
    Ⓑ 7 inches per day
    Ⓒ 3 inches per day
    Ⓓ $2\frac{2}{3}$ inches per day

2. **If your speed increased from 20 to 60 miles per hour in 7 seconds, what is the rate of change of your speed?**

    Ⓐ 5.7 m/s²
    Ⓑ 40 m/s²
    Ⓒ 20571 m/s²
    Ⓓ 6 m/s²

3. **Calculate the average rate of change of f(x)=3x²+7x−16 between x=3 and x=5.**

    Ⓐ 20.66
    Ⓑ 31
    Ⓒ 12.4
    Ⓓ 7.75

4. **Calculate the average rate of change of g(x)=$\frac{1}{2x}$−x² between x=−1 and x=5.**

    Ⓐ -6.6
    Ⓑ -5.85
    Ⓒ -4.4
    Ⓓ -3.9

5. Find the average rate of change for 4≤s≤10.

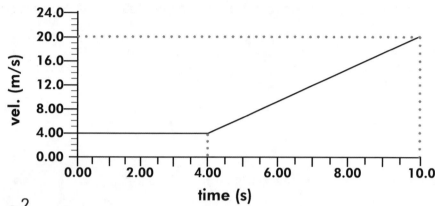

Ⓐ $2\frac{2}{3}$ m/s²

Ⓑ 3 m/s²

Ⓒ 2 m/s²

Ⓓ 0.375 m/s²

1. The graph of $f(x) = \frac{1}{10}(x+)(x-2)(x-5)$ is shown below. Over which interval is f(x) positive?

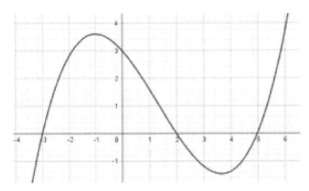

Ⓐ $(5, \infty)$
Ⓑ $(-\infty, -3) \cup (2, 5)$
Ⓒ $(-3, 2) \cup (5, \infty)$
Ⓓ $(-\infty, 3. -0.43)$

2. The graph of a transformed square root curve is in the figure below. What is the equation of the curve?

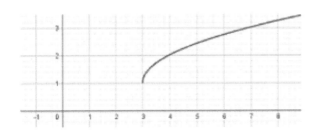

Ⓐ $y = \sqrt{x+3} + 1$
Ⓑ $y = \sqrt{x-3} + 1$
Ⓒ $y = \sqrt{x-3}$
Ⓓ $y = \sqrt{x} + 1$

3. The figure below shows a polynomial function's graph. How many zeros does the function have?

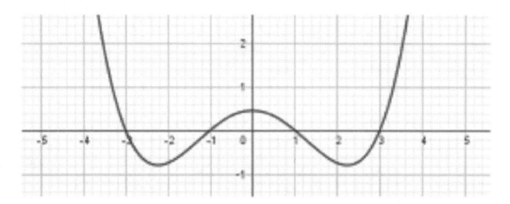

Ⓐ 3
Ⓑ 4
Ⓒ 5
Ⓓ 2

4. The figure below shows the graph of a quintic polynomial function. How many turning points does the function's graph have?

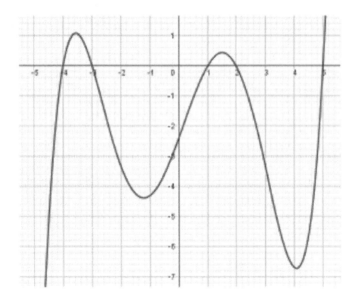

Ⓐ 3
Ⓑ 4
Ⓒ 5
Ⓓ 6

5. The graph of a transformed cube root curve is in the figure below. What is the equation of the curve?

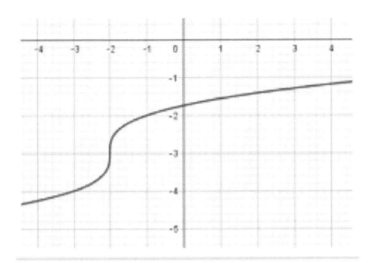

Ⓐ $y=\sqrt[3]{x-2}-3$
Ⓑ $y=\sqrt[3]{x+3}-2$
Ⓒ $y=\sqrt[3]{x+2}-3$
Ⓓ $y=\sqrt[3]{x-3}-2$

Lesson 9: Writing Functions in Different Forms to find Critical Information

1. Solve $5x^2 - 7x + 1 = 0$.

   Ⓐ $x = \dfrac{7 \pm \sqrt{29}}{10}$

   Ⓑ $x = \dfrac{-7 \pm \sqrt{29}}{10}$

   Ⓒ $x = \dfrac{7 \pm \sqrt{-29}}{10}$

   Ⓓ $x = \dfrac{7 \pm i\sqrt{29}}{10}$

2. We can write the equation for Kinetic Energy as $KE(v) = \dfrac{1}{2}mv^2$. We know that the vertex exists at $v = 0$. Rewrite the equation assuming an additional velocity of 3m/s.

   Ⓐ $KE(v) = \dfrac{1}{2}mv^2 + 3$

   Ⓑ $KE(v) = \dfrac{1}{2}(m+3)v^2$

   Ⓒ $KE(v) = \dfrac{1}{2}m(v+3)^2$

   Ⓓ None of these

3. The value of a house H after time t can be written as $H(t) = 1.06^t$. Is the value of the house growing or decaying for H(t).

   Ⓐ Decaying, 6% for each time interval t
   Ⓑ Growing, 6% for each time interval t
   Ⓒ Growing, 106% for each time interval t
   Ⓓ Growing, 60% for each time interval t

4. If the equation for the height of an object in projectile motion is written as $h(t) = -4t^2 + 5t$, what time will the object be at the highest point in its trajectory?

   Ⓐ $t = \dfrac{8}{5}$

   Ⓑ $t = 1$

   Ⓒ $t = \dfrac{5}{8}$

   Ⓓ $t = 0$

5. What are the x-intercepts of $y = 6x^2 + 2x$?

Lesson 10: Comparing properties of Functions

1. **Line a is represented by the equation y = 3x + 7 and line b contains the points (0, 1) and (3, 3). Which line has the greater slope?**

   Ⓐ Line b
   Ⓑ Neither, they have the same slope
   Ⓒ Line a
   Ⓓ Not enough information

2. **Which of the functions f(x)=x²−4 or g(x)=3ˣ−4 have the least possible y-value?**

   Ⓐ f(x)
   Ⓑ g(x)
   Ⓒ They both reach the same lowest value
   Ⓓ Not enough information

3. **List all the vertical asymptotes of the rational functions $f(x)=\dfrac{x-4}{x+2}$ and $g(x)=\dfrac{x+4}{x^2-4}$.**

   Ⓐ f(x)
   Ⓑ g(x)
   Ⓒ They both reach the same lowest value
   Ⓓ Not enough information

4. **Which of the following functions has more zeros?**

   $f(x)=x^3+4x^2-x-7$
   $g(x)=\dfrac{1}{4}(x+1)(x-1)(x+3)(x-2)(x-4)$

   Ⓐ f(x)
   Ⓑ g(x)
   Ⓒ They have the same amount of zeros
   Ⓓ They don't have any zeros

5. **If f(x) is a polynomial with an order of 6 and a y-intercept of -1 and g(x) is a linear function with an undefined slope, which function will cross the x-axis more?**

   Ⓐ They will both cross the x-axis once
   Ⓑ Neither one will cross the x-axis
   Ⓒ They will both cross the x-axis twice
   Ⓓ f(x) will cross more as it crosses twice while g(x) only crosses once

1. **Which function is graphed below?**

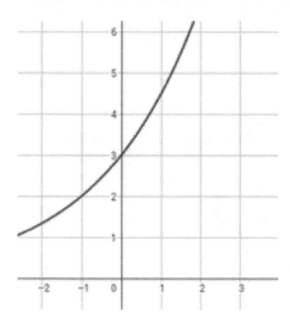

Ⓐ $f(x)=3(0.5)^x$
Ⓑ $f(x)=1.5(3)^x$
Ⓒ $f(x)=3(1.5)^x$
Ⓓ $f(x)=2(1.5)^x$

2. **Which function provides the values in the table below?**

x	1	2	3	4
y	1	4	9	16

Ⓐ $f(x)=x^2$
Ⓑ $f(x)=x^3$
Ⓒ $f(x)=2x$
Ⓓ $f(x)=\dfrac{1}{4}x^4$

3. Which function is graphed below?

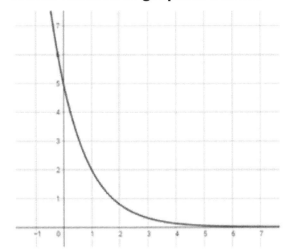

Ⓐ $f(x) = 5(0.5)^x$
Ⓑ $f(x) = 5(0.4)^x$
Ⓒ $f(x) = 4(0.5)^x$
Ⓓ $f(x) = 5(1.5)^x$

4. Which function provides the values in the table below?

x	1	2	3	4
y	-4	-8	-12	-16

Ⓐ $f(x) = -4x$
Ⓑ $f(y) = -4y$
Ⓒ $f(x) = 4x$
Ⓓ $f(x) = \dfrac{1}{4}y$

5. **Which function is graphed below?**

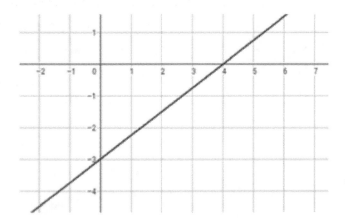

Ⓐ $f(x) = \dfrac{3}{4}x - 3$

Ⓑ $f(x) = \dfrac{3}{4}y - 3$

Ⓒ $f(x) = 3x - 3$

Ⓓ $f(x) = \dfrac{4}{3}x - 3$

Lesson 12: Linear Equations in Business

1. Suppose a construction company is preparing to build a large apartment complex and is beginning to receive truckloads of sheetrock (dry wall boards) for the project. The company has 550 sheets on hand and each truckload has 75 sheets. Which function P(t) represents the number of sheets of drywall the company has on hand if t truckloads of drywall have been delivered?

    Ⓐ P(t)=-75t+550
    Ⓑ P(t)=75t-550
    Ⓒ P(t)=75t+550
    Ⓓ P(t)=550t-75

2. Suppose there are 750 hamburger buns in the store room at a restaurant at the beginning of the week. The restaurant expects to sell 250 hamburgers each day. Which function H(b) represents the number of hamburger buns that will be in the store room after selling them for b days?

    Ⓐ H(b)=750-250b
    Ⓑ H(b)=-750+250b
    Ⓒ H(b)=750+250b
    Ⓓ H(b)=750b-250

3. The ABC Early Childhood Center will open for business with 64 students. Every year after opening the school expects to add 26 new students. Which function S(x) represents the number of students who will be enrolled at the school after x years?

    Ⓐ S(x)=-26+64x
    Ⓑ S(x)=64+26x
    Ⓒ S(x)=64-26x
    Ⓓ S(x)=64x+26

4. Suppose there are 448 graduates in a ceremony to receive their diplomas. The Dean of Graduation has already presented 56 diplomas and said he can present 5 diplomas per minute. Based on this information, which function D(h) represents the number of diplomas that have been presented after h hours?

    Ⓐ D(h)=448-300h
    Ⓑ D(h)=56+300h
    Ⓒ D(h)=448-5h
    Ⓓ D(h)=300+56h

5. Suppose a fundraising company had 2,500 notebooks for promotional gifts for a fund drive telethon. The fund drive had an early invitation for past donors and gave 750 of the notebooks away before the fund drive began. The fund drive sponsors expect a large amount of excitement about the drive and expect to give away 85 notebooks per hour during the drive. How many notebooks will they have left after the 20 hour telethon?

Lesson 13: Exponential Models Expressed as Logarithms

1. **When asked to covert from an exponential to logarithmic equation which type of logarithm should you use?**

   Ⓐ It doesn't matter
   Ⓑ Log base 10
   Ⓒ Natural log
   Ⓓ Not enough information given

2. **Solve the equation $e^{3x}=27$ using logarithmic form.**

   Ⓐ $x=\ln 9$
   Ⓑ $x=\dfrac{\ln 27}{3}$
   Ⓒ $x=9$
   Ⓓ None of these

3. **To find the log of an exponential function in the calculator convert $\log_b x = y$ into what form?**

   Ⓐ $\dfrac{\log x}{\log b}$
   Ⓑ $\dfrac{\ln x}{\ln b}$
   Ⓒ A or B
   Ⓓ None of these

4. **Convert $5e^x=120$ into logarithmic form.**

   Ⓐ $x=\ln 24$
   Ⓑ $x=\dfrac{\ln 120}{\ln 5}$
   Ⓒ $x=\dfrac{\ln 120}{5}$
   Ⓓ None of these

5. **Convert $3e^x=33$ into logarithmic form.**

   Ⓐ $x=\dfrac{\ln 33}{\ln 3}$
   Ⓑ $x=\ln 11$
   Ⓒ $x=\dfrac{\ln 33}{3}$
   Ⓓ None of these

Lesson 14: Radians, Degrees, and Arc Length

1. What is $\dfrac{2\pi}{3}$ radians in degrees?

   Ⓐ 270°
   Ⓑ 120°
   Ⓒ 119.939°
   Ⓓ 45°

2. What is the length, in inches, of an arc subtended by an angle of 36° on a circle with a radius of 15 inches?

   Ⓐ 540 inches
   Ⓑ 36π inches
   Ⓒ 36 inches
   Ⓓ 3π inches

3. What is the length, in centimeters, of an arc subtended by an angle of $\dfrac{2\pi}{7}$ radians on a circle with a radius of 14 centimeters?

   Ⓐ 14 cms
   Ⓑ π cms
   Ⓒ 4π cms
   Ⓓ 7π cms

4. What is 55° in radians?

   Ⓐ $\dfrac{36}{11\pi}$

   Ⓑ $\dfrac{11}{36\pi}$

   Ⓒ $\dfrac{11\pi}{36}$

   Ⓓ $\dfrac{36\pi}{11}$

5. What is $\dfrac{4\pi}{9}$ radians in degrees?

   Ⓐ 100°
   Ⓑ 75°
   Ⓒ 251.2°
   Ⓓ 80°

1. The terminal side of θ in standard position contains the point (-3, -4). Find the exact value of sin θ.

(A) $\dfrac{3}{4}$

(B) $-\dfrac{3}{5}$

(C) $-\dfrac{3}{4}$

(D) $-\dfrac{4}{5}$

2. The terminal side of θ in standard position contains the point (5, 12). Find the exact value of tan θ.

(A) $\dfrac{5}{12}$

(B) $\dfrac{12}{5}$

(C) $-\dfrac{5}{13}$

(D) $\dfrac{13}{5}$

3. Find the exact value of $\cos \dfrac{4\pi}{3}$.

(A) $\dfrac{1}{2}$

(B) $\dfrac{\sqrt{3}}{2}$

(C) $-\dfrac{1}{2}$

(D) $-\dfrac{\sqrt{3}}{2}$

4. Find the exact value of csc $\dfrac{5\pi}{6}$.

    Ⓐ -2

    Ⓑ 2

    Ⓒ $\dfrac{1}{2}$

    Ⓓ $-\dfrac{1}{2}$

5. If the terminal side of an angle in standard position passes through the point (3, 2), which ratio will be used to find the value of csc?

    Ⓐ $\dfrac{\sqrt{13}}{3}$

    Ⓑ $\dfrac{\sqrt{13}}{2}$

    Ⓒ $\dfrac{2\sqrt{13}}{2}$

    Ⓓ $\dfrac{3\sqrt{13}}{3}$

Lesson 16: Amplitude, Frequency, and Midlines

1. Which one of the following functions has a period of $\dfrac{8\pi}{3}$?

   Ⓐ $y = 2 \sin\left(\dfrac{4x}{3}\right) + 5$

   Ⓑ $y = 4 \tan\left(\dfrac{3x}{4}\right) - 1$

   Ⓒ $y = 2 \sin\left(\dfrac{3x}{4}\right) - 5$

   Ⓓ $y = \dfrac{8}{3} \sin(x) - 2$

2. What is the amplitude of the function $y = -2 \sin(x - \pi) + 3$?

   Ⓐ 2
   Ⓑ 4
   Ⓒ -2
   Ⓓ π

3. Which one of the following functions has a period of 5?

   Ⓐ $y = 7 \cos\left(\dfrac{\pi x}{5}\right)$

   Ⓑ $y = 4 \tan\left(\dfrac{x}{5}\right)$

   Ⓒ $y = -4 \cos\left(\dfrac{2\pi x}{5}\right)$

   Ⓓ $y = 12 \sin\left(\dfrac{5x}{\pi}\right)$

4. What is the period of the trigonometric function $y = -3 \sin\left(\dfrac{2x}{7}\right) + 6$?

   Ⓐ $\dfrac{2}{7}$

   Ⓑ 7π

   Ⓒ $\dfrac{2\pi}{7}$

   Ⓓ $\dfrac{6}{7}$

5. **Which one of the following functions has a period of π?**

Ⓐ $y = 5 \cos \left(\dfrac{x}{2} \right)$

Ⓑ $y = -3 \tan \left(\dfrac{x}{2} \right) + 1$

Ⓒ $y = -3 \sin (2x) + 1$

Ⓓ $y = 7 \sin \left(\dfrac{3x}{\pi} \right) + 6$

Lesson 17: Trigonometric Functions in the Quadrants

1. If θ is in quadrant IV, and $\sin \theta = -\dfrac{6}{10}$, what is $\tan \theta$?

   Ⓐ $-\dfrac{4}{3}$

   Ⓑ $\dfrac{5}{3}$

   Ⓒ $\dfrac{3}{4}$

   Ⓓ $-\dfrac{3}{4}$

2. If θ is in quadrant III, and $\cos \theta = -\dfrac{15}{17}$, what is $\sin \theta$?

   Ⓐ $\dfrac{8}{17}$

   Ⓑ $\dfrac{15}{17}$

   Ⓒ $-\dfrac{8}{17}$

   Ⓓ $\dfrac{17}{8}$

3. If θ is in quadrant IV, and $\cos \theta = \dfrac{5}{13}$, what is $\tan \theta$?

   Ⓐ $-\dfrac{12}{5}$

   Ⓑ $\dfrac{12}{5}$

   Ⓒ $\dfrac{12}{13}$

   Ⓓ $-\dfrac{5}{12}$

4. If θ is in quadrant III, and sin θ = $-\dfrac{24}{25}$, what is cos θ??

   (A) $\dfrac{24}{25}$

   (B) $-\dfrac{7}{25}$

   (C) $-\dfrac{24}{25}$

   (D) $\dfrac{24}{7}$

5. If θ is in quadrant II, and sin θ = $\dfrac{4}{5}$, what is cos θ?

   (A) $-\dfrac{4}{5}$

   (B) $\dfrac{5}{3}$

   (C) $-\dfrac{3}{5}$

   (D) $\dfrac{3}{5}$

End of Functions

Workbook
Chapter 4

Number and Quantity

1. **Find the product of 2+4i and 1−i. Simplify completely.**

   Ⓐ $2+2i+4i^2$
   Ⓑ $2-4i^2$
   Ⓒ 6
   Ⓓ $6+2i$

2. **Simplify completely $(2-3i)^2$**

   Ⓐ $13-12i$
   Ⓑ $4-12i-9i^2$
   Ⓒ $4-9i^2$
   Ⓓ $-5-12i$

3. **Simplify completely i(7−i)**

   Ⓐ $7i-i^2$
   Ⓑ $1+7i$
   Ⓒ $6i$
   Ⓓ $-1+7i$

4. **Simplify completely 6i(4i−3)**

   Ⓐ $24-18i$
   Ⓑ $-24+18i$
   Ⓒ $-24-18i$
   Ⓓ $24+18i$

5. **Simplify completely (4+3i)(4−3i)**

   Ⓐ $16+9i^2$
   Ⓑ $16-9i^2$
   Ⓒ 7
   Ⓓ 25

Lesson 2: Introduction to Imaginary and Complex Numbers

1. **What does 3 + 7i simplify to be?**

   Ⓐ 10i
   Ⓑ 21i
   Ⓒ 10i²
   Ⓓ 3+7i

2. **What does i² simplify to be?**

   Ⓐ -i
   Ⓑ i
   Ⓒ 1
   Ⓓ -1

3. **What does 2+6+4i simplify to be?**

   Ⓐ 2+10i
   Ⓑ 12i
   Ⓒ 8+4i
   Ⓓ 12+i

4. **What is the $\sqrt{-81}$?**

   Ⓐ −9
   Ⓑ −9i
   Ⓒ 9+i
   Ⓓ 9i

5. **Simplify the following $\sqrt{36}+\sqrt{-4}$**

   Ⓐ 8i
   Ⓑ 6+2i
   Ⓒ 6−2i
   Ⓓ 4i

Lesson 3: Solving Quadratic Equations with Real Coefficients that have Complex Solutions

1. **Solve for x in $x^2+4x+22=13$**

   Ⓐ $x=2\pm i\sqrt{5}$
   Ⓑ $x=-2\pm i\sqrt{5}$
   Ⓒ $x=-2\pm\sqrt{5}$
   Ⓓ $x=-2\pm 2i\sqrt{5}$

2. **Solve for x in $-5x^2-52=3$**

   Ⓐ $x=\pm\sqrt{11}$
   Ⓑ $x=\pm i\sqrt{11}$
   Ⓒ $x=-\sqrt{11}$
   Ⓓ $x=-i\sqrt{11}$

3. **Solve for x in $x^2+4x=-5$**

   Ⓐ $x=2\pm i$
   Ⓑ $x=-2+i$
   Ⓒ $x=-2-i$
   Ⓓ $x=-2\pm i$

4. **Solve for x in $-3x^2-9x-12=0$**

   Ⓐ $x=\dfrac{3\pm i\sqrt{7}}{2}$
   Ⓑ $x=\dfrac{-3\sqrt{7}}{2}$
   Ⓒ $x=\dfrac{-3\pm i\sqrt{7}}{2}$
   Ⓓ $x=\dfrac{3+i\sqrt{7}}{2}$

5. **Solve for x in $-2x^2-5x-2=4$**

   Ⓐ $x=\dfrac{5\pm i\sqrt{23}}{4}$
   Ⓑ $x=\dfrac{-5\pm i\sqrt{23}}{4}$
   Ⓒ $x=\dfrac{-5\pm\sqrt{23}}{4}$
   Ⓓ $x=\dfrac{-5\pm i\sqrt{23}}{2}$

Lesson 4: Recognizing Reasonable Answers to Word Problems

1. Jenna is buying cookies for a club party. At the store, she found three different packages: 2 pounds for $15, 3 pounds for $20, and 10 pounds for $60. She has $100 to spend. What is the maximum number of pounds of cookies Jenna can buy if she spends all of her money?

   Ⓐ $14
   Ⓑ $15
   Ⓒ $16
   Ⓓ $17

2. You need exactly 10 kg of corn or rice. The store has corn for $15 for 2 kg and rice for $20 for 3 kg. What is the least you must spend to buy exactly 10 kg?

   Ⓐ $55
   Ⓑ $60
   Ⓒ $70
   Ⓓ $75

3. For New Year, William wants to decorate his house with the decorative lighting. He needs 360ft of lighting to decorate the front of his house. He saw many lengths in the market. Which length of light strings, given their price, will allow him to decorate his house at the least cost?

   Ⓐ 10 feet − $17
   Ⓑ 12 feet − $43
   Ⓒ 20 feet − $34
   Ⓓ 30 feet − $45

4. Juanita says she drinks 3 cups of coffee, every day, Monday through Friday, at work. The office she works at has a coffee pool, and the pool buys coffee in cases of 120 individual k-cup pods for $39.60 per case. How much of the cost of coffee should Juanita pay per year if she is at work 49 weeks per year?

   Ⓐ $242.55
   Ⓑ $257.40
   Ⓒ $247.50
   Ⓓ $237.60

5. Your mother and your elder sister usually go to the store together. Yesterday, they found different sizes of packets of detergent powder: Small − 2kg for $6, Medium − 5kg for $8, and Large − 15kg for $18. If they have $50, and they spend it all on detergent powder, what is the maximum number of kilograms of detergent powder they can buy?

Lesson 5: Evaluating Rational Exponents

1. Which of the following expressions is an equivalent radical simplified expression for $16^{\frac{5}{4}}$?

   Ⓐ $2^{\frac{5}{2}}$
   Ⓑ 32
   Ⓒ 4^5
   Ⓓ 5

2. Which of the following expressions is an equivalent simplified radical exponent expression for $9^{\frac{2}{5}}$?

   Ⓐ 3^5
   Ⓑ $\sqrt{9^5}$
   Ⓒ $(\sqrt[5]{9})^2$
   Ⓓ $(\sqrt{9})^5$

3. Which of the following expressions is an equivalent simplified expression with a rational exponent for $(\sqrt[4]{17})^3$?

   Ⓐ $17^{\frac{4}{3}}$
   Ⓑ 17
   Ⓒ $17^{\frac{3}{4}}$
   Ⓓ $(\sqrt{17})^{\frac{3}{4}}$

4. Which of the following expressions is an equivalent simplified radical exponent expression for $18^{\frac{2}{5}}$?

   Ⓐ 3^5
   Ⓑ $(\sqrt[5]{18})^2$
   Ⓒ $(\sqrt[5]{9})^2$
   Ⓓ $(\sqrt{9})^5$

5. Which of the following expressions is an equivalent simplified expression for $(125^{\frac{3}{2}})^{\frac{4}{9}}$?

   Ⓐ $5^{\frac{2}{3}}$
   Ⓑ 25
   Ⓒ $125^{\frac{3}{2}}$
   Ⓓ 5

1. Fill in the blank with the correct number for the missing denominator in the following problem.

   $\sqrt[5]{625} = 625^{\frac{1}{?}}$?

2. Rewrite $\sqrt[3]{125}$ in exponential form.

   Ⓐ 125^{-3}
   Ⓑ 125^{3}
   Ⓒ $125^{\frac{1}{3}}$
   Ⓓ $125^{-\frac{1}{3}}$

3. Rewrite $x^{\frac{1}{2}}$ in radical form.

   Ⓐ $\sqrt{x}$
   Ⓑ $\sqrt{x^2}$
   Ⓒ $\dfrac{1}{\sqrt{x}}$
   Ⓓ $-\sqrt{x}$

4. Write the following in radical form $27^{\frac{2}{3}}$?

   Ⓐ $(\sqrt{27})^3$
   Ⓑ $(\sqrt[3]{27})^2$
   Ⓒ $\sqrt{27^3}$
   Ⓓ $\dfrac{1}{\sqrt[3]{27^2}}$

5. Write the following in exponential form $\sqrt[5]{x^2}$

   Ⓐ $x^{\frac{5}{2}}$
   Ⓑ $2x^5$
   Ⓒ $x^{\frac{1}{5}}$
   Ⓓ $x^{\frac{2}{5}}$

End of Number and Quantity

Answer Key
&
Detailed Explanations

Chapter 2: Algebra

Lesson 1: Remainder Theorem & Zeros of a Polynomial

Question No.	Answer Key	Detailed Explanation
1	B	The Remainder Theorem is based on synthetic division, which is the process of dividing a polynomial f (x) by a polynomial D(x) and finding the quotient and remainder. This process evaluates the polynomial f(x) at a value where x = -c if D(x) = x + c. We can divide $(3x^3 - 3x^2 + 2x + 14)$ by (x-2) Using synthetic division as: 2| 3 -3 2 14 / ↓ 6 6 16 / 3 3 8 [30] The remainder is the last number in the bottom row of the synthetic division. Therefore, f(2) = 30.
2	A	The Remainder Theorem is based on synthetic division, which is the process of dividing a polynomial f(x) by a polynomial D(x) and finding the quotient and remainder. This process evaluates the polynomial f(x) at a value where x = -c if D(x) = x + c. We can divide $(2x^2 - 5x - 3)$ by (x+4) Using synthetic division as: -4| 2 -5 -3 / ↓ -8 52 / 2 -13 [49] The remainder is the last number in the bottom row of the synthetic division and the function value. Therefore, g(-4) = 49.
3	C	The Remainder Theorem is based on synthetic division, which is the process of dividing a polynomial f(x) by a polynomial D(x) and finding the quotient and remainder. This process evaluates the polynomial f(x) at a value where x = c if D(x) = x - c. We can divide $(x^4 + x^3 - 3x^2 - 4x - 5)$ by (x-2) Using synthetic division as: 2| 1 1 -3 -4 -5 / ↓ 2 6 6 4 / 1 3 3 2 [-1] The remainder is the last number in the bottom row of the synthetic division and the function value. Therefore, h(2) = -1.

Question No.	Answer Key	Detailed Explanation
4	D	Student must substitute $x = 1$ and solve; if the substitution yields zero, there is no remainder; in this case $2(1)^3-5(1)+(1)-3=-5$.
5	B	Student must substitute -1 into the function as follows $-(-1)^3+6(-1)-7=-12$ and find the value to get the remainder
6	B	The question asks us to find the zeros of $(x^2+4x-12)$ First, we will factor h(x) as $(x+6)$ $(x-2)$. Next, we will set each factor equal to zero because the term "zeros of a function" means that the function has a value of zero: $x + 6 = 0$, $x = -6$; $x-2 = 0$, $x=2$. Thus, the zeros of the function are -6 and 2.
7	B	The question asks us to find the zeros of $f(x) = (x^3+16x^2+64x)$ First, we will factor f(x) as $x(x+8)(x+8)$ or $x(x+8)^2$ Next, we will set each factor equal to zero because the term "zeros of a function" means that the function has a value of zero: $x+8=0$, $x=-8$ and $x=0$. Thus, the function has two zeros, which are -8 and 0.
8	D	The question asks us to find the zeros of $g(x) = x^2+11x+18$ First, we will factor g(x) as $(x+9)(x+2)$. Next, we will set each factor equal to zero because the term "zeros of a function" means that the function has a value of zero: $x + 9 = 0$, $x = -9$; $x + 2 = 0$, $x = -2$. Thus, the zeros of the function are -9 and -2.
9	A	The question asks us to find the zeros of $f(x) = (x^2+ x - 90)$ First, we will factor f(x) as $(x+10)$ $(x-9)$. Next, we will set each factor equal to zero because the term "zeros of a function" means that the function has a value of zero. $x + 10 = 0$, $x = -10$; $x – 9 = 0$, $x = 9$. Thus, the zeros of the function are -10 and 9.
10	B	The question asks us to find the zeros of $h(x) = (x^2-13x+40)$ First, we will factor h(x) as $(x – 5)$ $(x – 8)$. Next, we will set each factor equal to zero because the term "zeros of a function" means that the function has a value of zero. $x – 5 = 0$, $x = 5$; $x – 8 = 0$, $x = 8$. Thus, the zeros of the function are 5 and 8.

Question No.	Answer Key	Detailed Explanation
1	B	The binomial theorem typically uses Pascal's Triangle to identify the coefficients and exponents when expanding a binomial. That triangles looks like this, and the last row is for the 3rd power:

1

1 1

1 2 1

1 3 3 1

To expand the binomial, multiply the two terms by the number in the triangle and the powers in the pattern below. Expanding the given binomial gives us:

$$(2x-y)^3 = 1[(2x)^3(-y)^0] + 3[(2x)^2(-y)^1] + 3[(2x)^1(-y)^2] + 1[(2x)^0(-y)^3]$$

The second term is
$3[(2x)^2(-y)^1]$ which multiplies out as
$3[(2x)^2(-y)^1] = 3(4)(x^2)(-y) = -12x^2y$
The second term is $-12x^2y$.

Question No.	Answer Key	Detailed Explanation
2	C	The binomial theorem typically uses Pascal's Triangle to identify the coefficients and exponents when expanding a binomial. That triangles looks like this, and the last row is for the 5th power:

1

1 1

1 2 1

1 3 3 1

1 4 6 4 1

1 5 10 10 5 1

To expand the binomial, multiply the two terms by the number in the triangle and the powers in the pattern below. Expanding the given binomial gives us:

$$(x+5)^5 = 1[(x)^5(5)^0] + 5[(x)^4(5)^1] + 10[(x)^3(5)^2] + 10[(x)^2(5)^3] + 5[(x)^1(5)^4] + 1[(x)^0(5)^5]$$

The fourth term is
$10[(x)^2(5)^3]$ which multiplies out as
$10[(5)^3(x)^2] = 1250x^2$ which is the fourth term.

Question No.	Answer Key	Detailed Explanation
3	C	The binomial theorem typically uses Pascal's Triangle to identify the coefficients and exponents when expanding a binomial. That triangles looks like this, and the last row is for the 4th power: 1 1 1 1 2 1 1 3 3 1 1 4 6 4 1 To expand the binomial, multiply the two terms by the number in the triangle and the powers in the pattern below. Expanding the given binomial gives us: $(2x^3+1)^4 =$ $1[(2x^3)^4(1)^0] + 4[(2x^3)^3(1)^1] + 6[(2x^3)^2(1)^2] + 4[(2x^3)^1(1)^3] + 1[(2x^3)^2(1)^4]$ The third term is $6[(2x^3)^2(1)^2]$ which multiplies out as $6[(2x^3)^2(1)^2] = 6(4x^6).1 = 24x^6$ which is the third term
4	B	The binomial theorem typically uses Pascal's Triangle to identify the coefficients and exponents when expanding a binomial. That triangles looks like this, and the last row is for the 6th power: 1 1 1 1 2 1 1 3 3 1 1 4 6 4 1 1 5 10 10 5 1 1 6 15 20 15 6 1 To expand the binomial, multiply the two terms by the number in the triangle and the powers in the pattern below. Expanding the given binomial gives us: $(x+1)^6 =$ $1[(x)^6(1)^0] + 6[(x)^5(1)^1] + 15[(x)^4(1)^2] + 20[(x)^3(1)^3] + 16[(x)^2(1)^4] + 6[(x)^1(1)^5] + 1[(x)^0(1)^6]$ The sixth term is $6[(x)^1(1)^5]$ which multiplies as $6x$

Question No.	Answer Key	Detailed Explanation
5	B	The binomial theorem typically uses Pascal's Triangle to identify the coefficients and exponents when expanding a binomial. That triangles looks like this, and the last row is for the 5th power:

$$1$$
$$1\ 1$$
$$1\ 2\ 1$$
$$1\ 3\ 3\ 1$$
$$1\ 4\ 6\ 4\ 1$$
$$1\ 5\ 10\ 10\ 5\ 1$$

To expand the binomial, multiply the two terms by the number in the triangle and the powers in the pattern below. Expanding the given binomial gives us:
$(3x-1)^5 =$

$1[(3x)^5(-1)^0] + 5[(3x)^4(-1)^1] + 10[(3x)^3(-1)^2] + 10[(3x)^2(-1)^3] + 5[(3x)^1(-1)^4] + 1[(3x)^0(-1)^5]$

The fourth term is $10[(3x)^2(-1)^3]$
which multiplies out as
$10[(3x)^2(-1)^3] = 10(3x)^2(-1)^3 = 10(9)(-1)x^2 = -90x^2$
The fourth term is $-90x^2$

Lesson 3: Rewrite Simple Rational Expressions

Question No.	Answer Key	Detailed Explanation
1	B	The question asks us to simplify the following rational expression. $$\frac{x+(x-y)^2-y}{(x-y)^3}$$ First, we will rearrange the numerator, and then we will separate the expression into two terms. Lastly, we will simplify each term by canceling common factors in the numerator and denominator. The steps in this process are: $$\frac{x+(x-y)^2-y}{(x-y)^3}=\frac{x-y+(x-y)^2}{(x-y)^3}=\frac{x-y}{(x-y)^3}+\frac{(x-y)^2}{(x-y)^3}$$ $$=\frac{1}{(x-y)^2}+\frac{1}{x-y}$$
2	C	The question asks us to simplify the following rational expression. $$\frac{3x^3+5x^2-7}{x^3}$$ First, we will separate the expression into three terms. Then, we will simplify each term by canceling common factors in the numerator and denominator. The steps in this process are: $$\frac{3x^3+5x^2-7}{x^3}=\frac{3x^3}{x^3}+\frac{5x^2}{x^3}-\frac{7}{x^3}=3+\frac{5}{x}-\frac{7}{x^3}$$
3	B	The question asks us to simplify the following rational expression. $$\frac{5x^2+6x-2}{2x^2}$$ First, we will separate the expression into three terms. Then, we will simplify each term by canceling common factors in the numerator and denominator. The steps in this process are: $$\frac{5x^2+6x-2}{2x^2}=\frac{5x^2}{2x^2}+\frac{6x}{2x^2}-\frac{2}{2x^2}=\frac{5}{2}+\frac{3}{x}-\frac{1}{x^2}$$

Question No.	Answer Key	Detailed Explanation
4	B	The question asks us to simplify the following rational expression. $$\frac{7(x+4)-3(x+4)^3}{(x+4)^2}$$ First, we will separate the expression into two terms. Then, we will simplify each term by canceling common factors in the numerator and denominator. The steps in this process are: $$\frac{7(x+4)-3(x+4)^3}{(x+4)^2} = \frac{7(x+4)}{(x+4)^2} - \frac{3(x+4)^3}{(x+4)^2} = \frac{7}{x+4} - 3(x+4)$$
5	B	The question asks us to simplify the following rational expression. $$\frac{9x^3 - 12x^2 + 15x}{3x^3}$$ First, we will separate the expression into three terms. Then, we will simplify each term by canceling common factors in the numerator and denominator. The steps in this process are: $$\frac{9x^3 - 12x^2 + 15x}{3x^3} = \frac{9x^3}{3x^3} - \frac{12x^2}{3x^3} + \frac{15x}{3x^3} = 3 - \frac{4}{x} + \frac{5}{x^2}$$

Question No.	Answer Key	Detailed Explanation
1	A	Student must define Simeon's age in terms of Brina's age as b + 2, then use the information given (product of the ages is 63) to set up the equation shown in answer choice A.
2	B	Student must set up the binomials to show the length and width being increased by x and that the new area resulting from their product is 130,000 (200 x 500 x 130% = 130,000)
3	A	Student set up an exponential equation ($y = ab^x$) using $150,000 as the initial amount and the growth rate of 5% and evaluate it at x = 4 to find the senior year TRB; $y = 150,000(1.05)^4$
4	67 hours	Student must create an inequality equation and solve as shown below, furthermore student must recognize that the answer requires rounding up to meet the requirements of the situation stated in the problem (i.e. 66 hours will not earn at least $2,000). Let h = # of hours $29.95h \geq \$2000$ $\dfrac{29.95h}{29.95} \geq \dfrac{\$2000}{29.95}$ $h \geq 66.7796$
5	Yes	Yes, one box of cake mix cost $4.10 (20.50/5) so 7 will cost $28.70, therefore she has enough money with her. Student must use the information given to create a direct variation equation and find the cost of one box of cake mix and then use the price to determine if she has enough money.

Question No.	Answer Key	Detailed Explanation
1	B	The question asks you to find the solution to 8x-8=96. Begin by adding 8 to both sides of the equation. This gives you 8x=104. Next, divide both sides by 8 and x=13.
2	D	The question asks you to find the solution to 6x+5=101. Begin by subtracting 5 from both sides of the equation. This gives you 6x=96. Next, divide both sides by 6 and x=16.
3	B	The question asks you to find the solution to $\frac{x}{5}-7=23$. Begin by adding 7 to both sides of the equation. This gives you $\frac{x}{5}=30$. Next, multiply both sides by 5 and x=150.
4	C	The question asks you to find the solution to $\frac{x}{3}+46=61$. Begin by subtracting 46 from both sides of the equation. This gives you $\frac{x}{3}=15$. Next, multiply both sides by 3 and x=45.
5	36	The question asks you to find the solution to $\frac{x}{3}+5=17$. Begin by subtracting 5 from both sides of the equation. This gives you $\frac{x}{3}=12$. Next, multiply both sides by 3 and x=36.

Lesson 6: Solve Linear Equations And Inequalities With One Variable

Question No.	Answer Key	Detailed Explanation
1	C	Student must solve this two-step equation by applying inverse operations; first add 4 to both sides of the equation resulting in $2x=14$, next divide by 2 on both sides to solve for x.
2	B	Student must solve this one-step equation by applying the inverse operation of multiplication; by multiplying both sides of the equation by 3 we see y's value is 216. $216/3 = 72$.
3	C	Student must apply the distributive property on the left side of the equation to get the simplified equation of $10x-35=15x-10$ and then solve by applying inverse operations; student must recognize the need to combine like terms and move terms from one side of the equation to the other, which yields: $-25=5x$; the final step is to divide both sides of the equation by 5 (apply the inverse).
4	B	Student must first recognize the need to combine like terms which requires moving terms from one side of the equation to the other; the final step tests for understanding of an inequality – the solution a student will get is $x>3$ however 3 is not an answer choice; student must recognize any number greater than 3 satisfies this inequality.
5	B	Student must first solve the one-step equation by applying the inverse operations of addition and then division resulting in the inequality $x<4$; answer choice B shows the positive integers less than 4.

Question No.	Answer Key	Detailed Explanation
1	D	The question asks you to find the solutions to the quadratic equation $2x^2+8x+6=0$. Find the solutions using factoring. In factoring, you factor the first and the third term in such a way that the two factors add to give the middle term. Since all of the terms can be divided by 2, simplify the quadratic equation to $x^2+4x+3=0$ Also, since all of the terms are positive, the two factors of that term must have a positive sign. Thus, the factored equation is $(x+1)(x+3)=0$. Find the solutions by making each factor equal to zero. $x+1=0$; $x=-1$ and $x+3=0$; $x=-3$.
2	C	The question asks you to find the solutions to the quadratic equation $4x^2+8x+4=0$. Find the solutions using factoring. In factoring, you factor the first and the third term in such a way that the two factors add to give the middle term. Since all of the terms can be divided by 4, simplify the quadratic equation to $x^2+2x+1=0$ Also, since all of the terms are positive, the two factors of that term must have a positive sign. Lastly, notice that the quadratic trinomial is a perfect square trinomial, in that the first and third terms are squares and the middle term is twice the product of the factors of the first and third terms. Thus, the factored equation is $(x+1)^2=0$. Find the solutions by making the factor equal to zero. $x+1=0$; $x=-1$.
3	B	To solve factor the equation as shown: $2x^2+9x-5=0$ $(2x-1)(x+5)=0$ $2x-1=0$ and $x+5=0$ $x=\frac{1}{2}$ and $x=-5$
4	A	To solve, factor the equation as shown: $x^2-9x+20=0$ $(x-4)(x-5)=0$ $x-4=0$ and $x-5=0$ $x=4$ and $x=5$
5	A	This problem can be easily solved by rearranging the equation so that it is solved for zero and then factoring out the greatest common factor $-8p$ and then solving for each factor as shown: $-8p^2=40p$ $-8p^2-40p=0$ $-8p(p+5)=0$ $p=0$ and $p=-5$

Question No.	Answer Key	Detailed Explanation
1	C	The elimination method (also known as the addition method) allows you to add the two equations together thereby eliminating one of the variables so that you can solve for the one that is left. Then use the one that you know to help you find the other one. $5x+2y=0$ $3x-2y=-16$ $8x=-16$ $x=-2$ Now use that x-value and plug back into one of the original two equations to find y. $5x+2y=0$ $5(-2)+2y=0$ $-10+2y=0$ $2y=10$ $y=5$ So then the final answer is $(-2, 5)$ or choice C.
2	D	If you solve the bottom equation for y, you get $y=4-x$. Then you can use substitution by plugging in $4-x$ in place of y in the first equation like so and then solve for x. $-2x=y-1$ $-2x=(4-x)-1$ $-2x=4-x-1$ $-2x=3-x$ $-x=3$ $x=-3$ Now use $x=-3$ and plug into one of the original equations to find y. $y+x=4$ $y+-3=4$ $y=7$ So the intersection point and final solution is $(-3, 7)$.

Question No.	Answer Key	Detailed Explanation
3	A	The question asks you to solve the system of equations below by replacing one equation with the sum of the two equations or by a multiple of the equation, and then adding the two equations together. $4x-3y=6$ $2x-5y=-4$ Multiply the second equation by -2. $4x-3y=6$ $-4x+10y=8$ Add the equations together to eliminate x and solve for y. $7y=14$ $y=2$ Substitute the value of y into one of the equations and solve for x. $4x-3(2)=6$ $4x-6=6$ $4x=12$ $x=3$ The solution to the system of equations is $(3,2)$.
4	$(2,-1)$	The question asks you to solve the system of equations below by replacing one equation with the sum of the two equations or by a multiple of the equation, and then adding the two equations together. $4x+5y=3$ $3x+2y=4$ Multiply the first equation by -2 and the second equation by 5. $-8x-10y=-6$ $15x+10y=20$ Add the equations together to eliminate y and solve for x. $7x=14$ $x=2$ Substitute the value of x into one of the equations and solve for y. $4(2)+5y=3$ $8+5y=3$ $5y=-5$ $y=-1$ The solution to the system of equations is $(2,-1)$.

Question No.	Answer Key	Detailed Explanation
1	$7.00	To solve this problem you need to set up a system of equations to represent the problem. We will use 'c' to represent the price of copper parts and 's' to represent the price of steel parts. The first equation would be based on this sentence from the problem: *A shipment containing 2 copper and 3 steel parts costs $26.* $2c+3s=26$ The second equation would be based on this sentence from the problem: *A second shipment containing 1 copper and 5 steel parts costs $27.* $c+5s=27$ There are many methods to solve this system of equations. Since we want to know the price of copper parts only, we will try and eliminate the 's' in the equations so that we can find 'c'. In order to do this using the addition method we will need to make the first equation have a 15s by multiplying the whole equation by 5 and then make the second equation have a -15s by multiplying the whole equation by -3.

First equation
$5(2c+3s=26)$
$10c+15s=130$

Second equation
$-3(c+5s=27)$
$-3c-15s=-81$

Now use the elimination (addition) method to find c.

$10c+15s=130$
$-3c-15s=-81$
$7c=49$
$c=7$

So the price of a copper part is $7.00.

Question No.	Answer Key	Detailed Explanation
2		Shelly mixed up the letters in her first equation. The sentence read: A shipment of 10 keyboards and 5 guitars costs $600, but Shelly wrote an equation for 5 keyboards and 10 guitars instead of the other way around. Simply switch the letters in her first equation and you have the correct setup for this problem. $10k + 5g = 600$ $2k + 8g = 470$ Now we can multiply the second equation by -5 so that the k's will be opposites and eliminate each other when the two equations are added. $-5(2k + 8g = 470)$ $-10k - 40g = -2350$ Now take this modified equation and add it to the original first equation $10k + 5g = 600$ $-10k - 40g = -2350$ $-35g = -1750$ $g = 50$ Now use the fact that g = 50 and plug back into one of the original equations to find k. $10k + 5g = 600$ $10k + 5(50) = 600$ $10k + 250 = 600$ $10k = 600 - 250$ $10k = 350$ $k = 35$ So, the cost of a keyboard is $35 and the cost of a guitar is $50.
3	The cost of a bunny rabbit is $12 and that of a goldfish is $5.	To solve a system of equations using the matrix method, you must set up a matrix that models the problem with using only the coefficients from the system of equations. Since there would be two equations and each one would have three terms, this will be a 2×3 matrix. The two equations would be $2b + 8g = 64$ $5b + 5g = 85$ The matrix will closely resemble the equations but with no letters and no mathematical symbols (ie. $+$, $-$, $=$). You could use your calculator to then solve this problems if needed.

Question No.	Answer Key	Detailed Explanation
4	D	Let x represent the first number and y represent the second number. Then the two equations would be as follows

$$x+y=24$$
$$x-y=6$$

Using the elimination (addition) method, you could eliminate the y's and solve for x.

$$x+y=24$$
$$x-y=6$$
$$2x=30$$
$$x=15$$

Now use the fact that x=15 and plug that value into one of the original equations to find y.

$$x+y=24$$
$$15+y=24$$
$$y=9$$

So the intersection point and final solution to the system of equations is (15,9).

| 5 | C | Convert each equation to slope-intercept form. The system becomes: |

$$y=-3x+4$$
$$y=3x-2$$

For each equation, plot the y-intercept point, and use the slope to find another point on the line. Then, identify the point where the two lines intersect. The graph of this system of equations is below.

Notice that the two lines intersect at the point (1,1).

Question No.	Answer Key	Detailed Explanation
1	A	The question asks you to find the point, in the first quadrant, where the functions $f(x)=x^2+8x-15$ and $g(x)=-x^2+4x+15$ intersect. Set the functions equal to each other and solve for x. Then substitute that answer into one of the functions to find y. $x^2+8x-15=-x^2+4x+15$; $2x^2+4x-30=0$; $x^2+2x-15=0$ Factor and solve this equation. $(x-3)(x+5)=0$; $x-3=0$; $x=3$; $x+5=0$; $x=-5$. Select $x=3$ to be in the first quadrant. $f(3)=3^2+8(3)-15=18$. The two curves intersect at the point (3,18).
2	D	The question asks you to find the point, in the first quadrant, where the functions $f(x)=3x^2-9x-6$ and $g(x)=2x^2-6x+4$ intersect. Set the functions equal to each other and solve for x. Then substitute that answer into one of the functions to find y. $3x^2-9x-6=2x^2-6x+4$; $x^2-3x-10=0$ Factor and solve this equation. $(x-5)(x+2)=0$; $x-5=0$; $x=5$; $x+2=0$; $x=-2$. Select $x=5$ to be in the first quadrant. $f(5)=3(5)^2-9(5)-6=24$. The two curves intersect at the point (5,24).
3	B	The question asks you to find the point that is closest to (0,0) where the two functions $f(x)=5x^2+25x+60$ and $g(x)=4x^2+6x$ intersect. Set the functions equal to each other and solve for x. Then substitute that answer into one of the functions to find y. $5x^2+25x+60=4x^2+6x$; $x^2+19x+60=0$ Factor and solve this equation. $(x+15)(x+4)=0$; $x+15=0$; $x=-15$; $x+4=0$; $x=-4$. Select $x=-4$ to be closer to the origin. $f(-4)=5(-4)^2+25(-4)+60=40$. The two curves intersect, closest to the origin, at the point (-4,40).
4	C	The question asks you to find the point that is closest to (0,0) where the two functions $f(x)=2x^2-7x+39$ and $g(x)=x^2+7x-1$ intersect. Set the functions equal to each other and solve for x. Then substitute that answer into one of the functions to find y. $2x^2-7x+39=x^2+7x-1$; $x^2-14x+40=0$ Factor and solve this equation. $(x-10)(x-4)=0$; $x-10=0$; $x=10$; $x-4=0$; $x=4$. Select $x=4$ to be closer to the origin. $f(4)=2(4)^2-7(4)+39=43$. The two curves intersect, closest to the origin, at the point (-4,43).
5	A	Your point of intersection must be proved to work in BOTH equations in order to prove that it is truly the intersection point.

Lesson 11: Solve Simple Rational and Radical Equations In One Variable

Question No.	Answer Key	Detailed Explanation
1	B	The question asks you to solve the radical equation $\sqrt{x}=0.9$. Solve this equation by squaring both sides. $(\sqrt{x})^2=(0.9)^2$. Squaring cancels the square root, so the answer is $x=0.81$.
2	D	The question asks you to solve the radical equation $\sqrt{4x-3}=\sqrt{5x}$. Solve this equation by squaring both sides. $(\sqrt{4x-3})^2=(\sqrt{5x})^2$. Squaring cancels the square root, so the equation changes to $4x-3=5x$. Subtract 4x from both sides and you have $x=-3$. However, if you substitute $x=-3$ into the original equation, you have $\sqrt{-15}=\sqrt{-15}$. You cannot take the square root of a negative number in the real number system. Therefore, there is to the equation.
3	D	The question asks you to solve the rational equation $\dfrac{2}{x+6}=\dfrac{-6}{x-4}$ This equation is a proportion, so solve it by cross multiplying. This gives you $2x-8 = -6x-36$. Next, add 6x to both sides and add 8 to both sides, resulting in $8x=-28$. Now, divide both sides by 8 and $x=-\dfrac{28}{8}=-\dfrac{7}{2}$.
4	C	The question asks you to solve the radical equation $\sqrt{x}=0.36$. Solve this equation by squaring both sides. $(\sqrt{x})^2=(0.36)^2$. Squaring cancels the square root, so the answer is $x=0.1296$.
5	A	The question asks you to solve the radical equation $\sqrt{9y-5}=\sqrt{7y}$. Solve this equation by squaring both sides. $(\sqrt{9y-5})^2=(\sqrt{7y})^2$. Squaring cancels the square root, so the equation changes to $9y-5=7y$. Subtract 9y from both sides and you have $-2y=-5$. Divide both sides by -2 and $y=\dfrac{5}{2}$. If you substitute $y=\dfrac{5}{2}$ into the original equation, you have $\sqrt{\dfrac{35}{2}}=\sqrt{\dfrac{35}{2}}$. Therefore, the solution to the equation is $y=\dfrac{5}{2}$.

Lesson 12: Solve a Simple System Consisting of a Linear Equation and a Quadratic Equation

Question No.	Answer Key	Detailed Explanation
1	C	The question asks you to solve this system of equations algebraically. $$y=-2$$ $$x^2+y^2=16$$ Substitute -2 into the second equation for y and solve for x. $$x^2+y^2=16$$ $$x^2+(-2)^2=16$$ $$x^2+4=16$$ $$x^2=12$$ $$x=\pm\sqrt{12}$$
2	B	The question asks you to solve this system of a quadratic equation and a linear equation algebraically. $$x=2$$ $$x^2+y^2=25$$ Substitute 2 into the second equation for x and solve for y. $$x^2+y^2=25$$ $$2^2+y^2=25$$ $$4+y^2=25$$ $$y^2=21$$ $$y=\pm\sqrt{21}$$
3	A	In order to be a solution to a system that only included the circle and the parabola, we would look for intersection points of those two graphs only. There are four separate intersection points for those two graphs as shown, $(-2, 1)$, $(1, -2)$, $(2, 1)$, $(-1, -2)$.

Question No.	Answer Key	Detailed Explanation
4	D	To find the points of intersection, set the functions equal to each other and solve for x.

$4x^2 - 4 = 3x$
$4x^2 - 3x - 4 = 0$

Now use the quadratic formula and values from the simplified equation above, $a = 4$, $b = -3$, $c = -4$

$$x = \frac{-(-3) \pm \sqrt{(-3)^2 - 4(4)(-4)}}{2(4)} = \frac{3 \pm \sqrt{73}}{8}$$

$x = \frac{3 + \sqrt{73}}{8}$ and $x = \frac{3 - \sqrt{73}}{8}$

$x = 1.44$ and $-.69$

These are the x-values for the points of intersection. You will need to plug each of them back into one of the original equations to find the y-values of each point.

$y = 3x$
$y = 3(1.44) = 4.32$

So the first intersection point is (1.44, 4.32).

$y = 3x$
$y = 3(-.69) = -2.07$ The second intersection point is (-.69, -2.07).

Question No.	Answer Key	Detailed Explanation
5	C	To find the points of intersection, set the functions equal to each other and solve for x.

$-5x^2 + 3 = 2x + 5$
$-5x^2 - 2x - 2 = 0$

By looking at the discriminant we can see if the two functions intersect and how many times.

$b^2 - 4ac = (-2)^2 - 4(-5)(-2) = -36$

Since the discriminant is negative there would be no real solutions and the graphs would not intersect.

Lesson 13: Interpret Parts Of An Expression

Question No.	Answer Key	Detailed Explanation
1	B	A factor is a number that when multiplied gives another number or an expression. The given expression $36x^2+12x+24$ can be factored as $12(3x^2+x+2)$ which shows that 12 is a factor of the given expression.
2	D	The expression $5x^3y^4+7x^2y^3-6xy^2-8xy$ is a polynomial expression with four terms. The coefficient of a term is the number in the front of the term. If the term begins with a negative, then the coefficient is a negative number, whether or not the term has variables. The third term is $-6xy^2$ and the number in the front of the term is -6.
3	B	The question asks us what the interest rate is in the expression $500(1.025)^7$. This expression uses the formula $P(1+r)^t$ where r is the annual interest rate as a decimal. Therefore, we will write an equation and solve for r: $1.025=1+r$; $r=0.025$. Since r is the interest rate as a decimal, we will multiply our answer by 100 and add the percent symbol. The interest rate is $0.025\times100=2.5\%$.
4	C	The question asks us how many years money was in an account in the expression $1500(1.0355)^9$. This expression uses the formula $P(1+r)^t$ where P is the principal in the account, r is the annual interest rate as a decimal, and t is the time in years. Therefore, since the given expression contains an exponent of 9, the money was in the account for 9 years.
5	C	The expression $12a^3b^2c^6+7abc-5a^2bc$ is a trinomial expression, meaning it has three terms. The numeric coefficient of a term is the number in front of the term. The third term is $-5a^2bc$ and the number in the front of the term is -5.

Lesson 14: Rewriting Expressions

Question No.	Answer Key	Detailed Explanation
1	A	Because multiplication obeys the commutative property (order doesn't matter), the middle terms in the given expression are like terms, which means they can be combined. Thus, an equivalent expression is $6y^2-3xy+5yx+13y^2 = 6y^2+2xy+13y^2$.
2	$3a(3b+1)(b-1)$	Student must first factor out the greatest common factor of $3a$, then factor the quadratic trinomial into binomials as shown below: $9ab^2 - 6ab - 3a$ $= 3a(3b^2 - 2b - 1)$ $= 3a(3b+1)(b-1)$
3		No, he did not. If you multiply the factors you will not get $\tan^3 x - 16\tan x$; the exponent of 3 is incorrect, the answer should be $\tan x(\tan x + 4)(\tan x - 4)$. Student needs to recognize that after factoring out the GCF of $\tan x$ you are left with the difference of two perfect squares which get factored into binomials; student may find it difficult to rewrite this given the use of trig-ratios, but the rule applies regardless.
4		Student must know how to factor by grouping to rewrite this expression as follows: $d^4 - 4d^2 + 8d^3 - 32d + 12d^2 - 48$ $d^2(d^2 - 4) + 8d(d^2 - 4) + 12(d^2 - 4)$ $(d^2 - 4)(d^2 + 8d + 12)$ $(d + 2)(d - 2)(d + 2)(d + 6)$ $(d + 2)^2(d - 2)(d + 6)$ Therefore, the correct answers are $(d + 6)$, $(d + 2)$ and $(d - 2)$.
5	False	The expression is a prime polynomial but not for the reason stated above; a prime polynomial is one that has only itself and 1 as factors.

For Question 4:

	d + 6	d - 6	d + 2	d - 2	d + 4
$d^4-4d^2+8d^3-32d+12d^2-48$	✓		✓	✓	

Lesson 15: Writing Expressions In Equivalent Forms

Question No.	Answer Key	Detailed Explanation
1	A	Student must solve for x by setting the factors equal to zero individually and then applying inverse operations
2	C	Student must demonstrate knowledge of the steps to completing the square; shown properly answer choice c properly shows that -16 has been added to both sides of the equation and the value of b has been halved, squared and added to both sides of the equation as well.
3	D	Student must understand that the expression given can be rewritten in factored form; the factors here are the difference of two perfect squares
4	A	Student must know how to set up an exponential equation that models depreciation; student must recall $y=ab^x$ is used and that $0<b<1$ for exponential decay problems.
5	B	Student must recognize that the prediction in years requires a change be made to the growth/decay factor and then compute $(.75)^{1/10} \approx .9716$ to find the answer.

Lesson 16: Finding The Sum of a Finite Geometric Series

Question No.	Answer Key	Detailed Explanation
1	C	In a geometric series $a_1=3$, $r=2$. The general formula for the sum of first n terms of a geometric series is $S_n=\frac{a_1(1-r^n)}{1-r}$. Therefore, the formula for the sum of the first six terms is $S_6=\frac{3(1-2^6)}{1-2}=\frac{3(-63)}{-1}=189$
2	B	In a geometric series if we divide any term by its previous term, we will find the common ratio r in the series. Thus, $r=\frac{-150}{-30}=5$. The general formula for the sum of first n terms of a geometric series is $S_n=\frac{a_1(1-r^n)}{1-r}$. Therefore, the formula for the sum of the first eight terms is $S_8=\frac{-6(1-5^8)}{1-4}=\frac{-6(1-390625)}{-4}=-585,936$
3	D	In a geometric series $a_1=-6$, $r=-3$. The general formula for a geometric series is $S_n=\frac{a_1(1-r^n)}{1-r}$. Therefore, the formula for the sum of the first ten terms is $S_{10}=\frac{-6(1-(-3)^{10})}{1-(-3)}=\frac{-6(-59048)}{4}=88,572$
4	A	In a geometric series $a_1=2$, $a_2=6$, $a_3=18$. If we divide any term by its previous term, we will find the common ratio r in the series. Thus, $r=\frac{18}{6}=3$. The general formula for the sum of first n terms of a geometric series is $S_n=\frac{a_1(1-r^n)}{1-r}$. Therefore, the formula for the sum of the first twelve terms is $S_{12}=\frac{2(1-3^{12})}{1-3)}=\frac{2(1-531441)}{-2}=531,440$
5	B	The general formula for the sum of first n terms of a geometric series is $S_n=\frac{a_1(1-r^n)}{1-r}$, using $n=10$, $r=-2$ and $a_1=3$

Answer Key
&
Detailed Explanations

Chapter 3: Functions

Lesson 1: Writing Functions that Describe a Relationship Between Two Quantities

Question No.	Answer Key	Detailed Explanation
1	C	Student must know the terms leading coefficient, constant and degree; the leading coefficient is the number multiplied by the variable with the highest exponent, the degree is the highest exponent in the expression and a constant is a term with no variables (a number).
2	C	Student must set up an expression that subtracts the cost of the gloves from the total cost in order to represent the cost of the baseball bat; student must use the coefficient of 2 because there are two gloves being purchased.
3	B	Student must understand that consecutive even integers are separated by 2 units on the number line, making x - 5, the next number after x - 7, to yield the next consecutive even number; student might substitute in a number for x that yields an even integer and then test the answers as an alternative way to answer this question as well.
4	B	Student must know there are 12 inches in 1 foot and then further recognize that the number of feet needs to be multiplied by 12 in order to find out how many inches are in a given number of feet.
5	D	Perimeter of a triangle is the sum of the length of all the sides. In an equilateral triangle, perimeter can be found by multiplying the length of one side by 3 as all the three sides are equal in an equilateral triangle. Therefore, $P=(x+5)+(x+5)+(x+5)$ or $P = 3(x+5)$ or $P = 3x + 15$

Lesson 2: Writing Arithmetic and Geometric Sequences

Question No.	Answer Key	Detailed Explanation
1	512 ft.	The ball falls 4ft, 8ft and 16ft in 1st, 2nd and 3rd second respectively. By looking at the number pattern of 4,8,16 we can say that it is a geometric sequence. Hence, the nth term will be given by $a_n = ar^{(n-1)}$ where a^n is the nth term; a is the first term i.e 4 and r is the common ratio $=\dfrac{16}{8}=\dfrac{8}{4}=2$ To find the distance the ball will fall in 8th second, substitute n=8, a=4 and r=2 in the above equation to get $a_8=4\times2^{(8-1)}$ $a_8=4\times2^7$ $a_8=512$ Thus, the ball will fall 512ft in the 8th second. Alternate explanation To solve this problem, you will need to find the pattern and extend it as shown 1st second: 4 2nd second: $4\times2=8$ 3rd second: $8\times2=16$ 4th second: $16\times2=32$ 5th second: $32\times2=64$ 6th second: $64\times2=128$ 7th second: $128\times2=256$ 8th second: $256\times2=512$
2		Jonathan's equation does not hold true past f(2) as shown below $f(n)=2n$ $f(1)=2\times1=2$ $f(2)=2\times2=4$ $f(3)=2\times3=6$ Since 6 is not a part of the sequence, this can't be the correct function to represent this sequence. Now let's check the first 3 terms of the new function. Given $f(1)=2$ $f(n+1)=2\times f(n)$, with $f(1)=2$ $f(2)=2\times2=4$ $f(3)=2\times4=8$ $f(4)=2\times8=16$

Question No.	Answer Key	Detailed Explanation
3		

Term #	Terms in sequence
1	1
2	6
3	11
4	16
30	**146**

By looking at the numbers 1,6,11,16.. we can say that each term is obtained by adding 5 to the previous term. Hence, this sequence is an arithmetic sequence where the first term, a=1 and common difference, d = 5.

n^{th} term of an arithmetic sequence is given by $a_n = a + (n-1)d$

Thus, $a_{30} = 1 + (30-1)5$

$a_{30} = 146$

Alternate explanation
The pattern here is to add 5 to the previous term, with the exception of term 1 which is given. You will need to extend this pattern to the 30th term. The explicit and recursive equation would be f(n+1)=f(n)+5, but since we need the 29th term to find the 30th term, we will have to extend the pattern all the way out as shown below starting with term 5.

21, 26, 31, 36, 41, 46, 51, 56, 61, 66, 71, 76, 81, 86, 91, 96, 101, 106, 111, 116, 121, 126, 131, 136, 141, 146

Question No.	Answer Key	Detailed Explanation
4	B	Allowance in the first few years will be -> \$10, \$12.50, \$15, \$17.50... This is an arithmetic sequence with the first term, $a = 10$ and common difference, $d = 2.50$ n^{th} term of an arithmetic sequence is given by $a_n = a + (n-1)d$ Thus, $a_n = 10 + (n-1)2.50$ $a_n = 10 + 2.50n - 2.50$ $a_n = 7.50 + 2.50n$ <u>Alternate explanation</u> The first year you will get \$10, so you have to pick the function that has a function value of 10 when you plug in a 1 for n. This eliminates choices A and D as these both give a value of \$12.50 when you plug in a 1 for n. To find the correct answer between B and C, we will need to plug in a 2. The second year you should get \$12.50. The only one that gives you \$12.50 when you plug in a 2 for n is answer choice B.
5	D	A recursive function finds the next term based on the previous term. In order to define a proper recursive function you must state the value of the first term so that it can be used to find the second term. The choice that states this recursive function properly is answer D. Choice A has the P(y) and P(y−1) mixed up. Answers B and C have an exponent still which will not be needed since a recursive function uses the previous terms value to find the next term.

Lesson 3: Transformation of Functions

Rule for Question No.1,2,3:

When functions are written in the form such as $f(x)=a(x-h)^2+k$, the values a, h, and k, each cause specific transformations to the function.

a causes a vertical stretch if $|a|>1$

a causes a vertical shrink if $0<|a|<1$

a causes a reflection of the graph across the x-axis if $a < 0$

h shifts the graph horizontally

if h is positive, the graph is translated to the right

if h is negative, the graph is translated to the left

k shifts the graph vertically

if $k > 0$, the graph is translated up

if $k < 0$, the graph is translated down

A function is even if $f(-x)=f(x)$. Even functions are symmetrical across the y-axis.

An function is odd if $f(-x)=-f(x)$. Odd functions are symmetrical about the origin, not across either axis.

Question No.	Answer Key	Detailed Explanation
1	odd	Based on our rules above, if we substitute -x into f(x), we would get 2(-x) which is -2x. Therefore, f(-x) = -2x. Since that shows that f(x) = -f(x), this indicates that the function is odd.
2		*(see table below)*

x	f(x)	g(x)
0	0	3
1	1	4
-1	-1	2
8	8	11

According to the rules, the k-value, which is 3, causes the graph to shift vertically. Therefore, each y-value in the f(x) function will be increased by 3. So, when f(x) = 0, g(x) = 3. When f(x) = 1, g(x) = 4. When f(x) = -1, g(x) = 2. When f(x) = 8, g(x) = 11.

3

f(x)	g(x)
0	-2
4	-8
¼	0
1	-½

According to our rules, the a-value controls two transformations, the vertical stretch or shrink and the reflection. Since the a-value, -2, is < 0, the graph will be reflected across the x-axis so the values of the function will be negative for each x-value. Also, since $|-2| = 2$, the g(x) will have a vertical stretch.

Question No.	Answer Key	Detailed Explanation
4	3	The vertical stretch is the A value when a quadratic is in standard form ($Ax^2 + Bx + C$).
5		y_2 has the same slope as y_1 but it is shifted 7 units down from y_1 When an equation is in slope-intercept form, $y = mx + b$, as these are, the m-value beside the x controls the slope of the equation. The b-value at the end is the y-intercept and controls the vertical shift (up or down). In these equations the m doesn't change so the slope doesn't change but the b changes from 0 to -7 which is a downward shift.

Lesson 4: Finding Inverse Functions

Question No.	Answer Key	Detailed Explanation
1	C	Rule #1: To find the inverse of a relation: Example #1 $f(x)=\{(1,2),(3,4),(-5,7)\}$. To find $f^{-1}(x)$, switch the x and y values in the ordered pairs. So $f^{-1}(x)=\{(2,1),(4,3),(7,-5)\}$ Example #2 When the function is in equation form such as $f(x)=3x-4$. To find $f^{-1}(x)$ switch x and y in $y=3x-4$ and then solve for y. $x=3y-4$ $y=\dfrac{x-4}{3}$ Therefore $f^{-1}(x)=\dfrac{x-4}{3}$ According to Example #2, to find the inverse of a function, you switch the x and y values in the equation and solve for y.
2	C	To find the inverse, we first need to change the function notation f(x) to a y and then switch the x and y in the equation and solve for y as shown below. $y=\sqrt{3x}-2$ $x=\sqrt{3y}-2$ $x+2=\sqrt{3y}$ $(x+2)^2=3y$ $\dfrac{(x+2)^2}{3}=y$
3	A	If we switch the x and y in the function, we end up with $x=3^y$. The only way to solve for y is to take the log. We know that $a=b^c$ means $\log_b a=c$. Using that same rule for this inverse function we end up with answer choice A.
4	D	Since we are told that the function is linear, we should know that the inverse of a linear functions will have points with the x and y coordinates switched. Since one of these (4, -1), (7, 2), or (10, 5) are in the answer choices, then we have our answer. If one of these switched around points were not in the answer choices, then we would have had to find the original equation, then the inverse and then find a points that worked
5	A	The function intersects the x-axis at its line of symmetry x = 0. The domain of the original function correlates to the range of the inverse function. Since our inverse function is $f^{-1}(x)=\sqrt{x}$, and there's no value of x that will make $f^{-1}(x)$ less than 0, that means the domain of our original function should be all values greater than or equal to 0, or A.

Lesson 5: Recognizing that Sequences are Functions

Question No.	Answer Key	Detailed Explanation
1	A	A recursive formula uses the previous term to find the next term. In an arithmetic sequence, the recursive formula is: $a_n = a_{n-1} + d$, where n is the term number and d is the common difference between each term. The given sequence is an arithmetic sequence, where each term is 14 more than the previous term, so the common difference is 14. Therefore, to find the next term, add 14 to the previous term, giving a formula of: $a_n = a_{n-1} + 14$.
2	A	A recursive formula uses the previous term to find the next term. In a geometric sequence, the recursive formula is: $a_n = a_{n-1} \times r$, where n is the term number and r is the common ratio between each term. The given sequence is a geometric sequence, where each term is 6 times the previous term, so the common ratio is 6. Therefore, to find the next term, multiply the previous term by 6, giving a formula of: $a_n = a_{n-1} \times 6$.
3	A	A recursive formula uses the previous term to find the next term. In a geometric sequence, the recursive formula is: $a_n = a_{n-1} \times r$, where n is the term number and r is the common ratio between each term. The given sequence is a geometric sequence, where each term is -4 times the previous term, so the common ratio is -4. Therefore, to find the next term, multiply the previous term by -4, giving a formula of: $a_n = a_{n-1} \times -4$.
4	C	The question asks us for formula for this sequence 1,2,2,4,8,32,256... in the domain n>2. This means our formula must be satisfied beginning with the third term in the sequence because n is the term number. In a sequence, a_n represents the value of the nth term. Notice that in the given sequence. $a_1 = 1$, $a_2 = 2$, $a_3 = 2$, $a_4 = 4$, $a_5 = 8$, $a_6 = 32$, $a_7 = 256$, ... Now notice that $a_1 = 1$, $a_2 = 2$, $a_3 = 2 = a_1 \times a_2$; $a_4 = 4 = a_2 \times a_3$; $a_5 = 8 = a_3 \times a_4$; $a_6 = 32 = a_4 \times a_5$ ... Therefore, the rule for the given sequence is $a_n = a_{n-2} \times a_{n-1}$.
5	34	In order to find the next number in the Fibonacci sequence we need to add the two previous terms. We are given the first 7 terms, (1, 1, 2, 3, 5, 8, 13....) So to find the 8th term we need to add the 6th and 7th terms and get 8 + 13 = 21. Then to find the 9th term we need to add the 7th and 8th terms and get 13 + 21 = 34. So the 9th term in the Fibonacci sequence is 34.

Question No.	Answer Key	Detailed Explanation
1	A	The company's goal is for the call center process 10 new customers per hour. Notice that the table shows that only during hour 4 the number of new customers processed meets or exceeds 10.
2	C	The table shows customer complaints and compliments per shift. The shift labeled "Noon to 6pm" received the next to the lowest complaints but the most compliments. Based on this information, we can conclude that this shift is doing the best job.
3	C	Based on the data in the table, add the number of people arriving and subtract the number of people departing. Carry that number to the next period and repeat the process for the rest of the day. The number of people at the contest at the end of each two-hour period is shown in the table below.

Time	Arriving per Hour	Departing per Hour
8:00-10:00	260	80
10:00-12:00	175	90
12:00-2:00	160	100
2:00-4:00	120	150
4:00-6:00	90	195
6:00-8:00	20	210

Notice that the most people are at the contest during 12:00pm - 2:00pm.

Question No.	Answer Key	Detailed Explanation
4	84	The company awards 5 points for every 100 holes whose depth is within specifications, and then subtracts one point for each hole that is not within specification. The table below shows the data for each drill press operator.

Operator	#Within Specs	Add points	#Not within Specs	Subtract points	Net
Joe	1300	65	6	-6	59
Pete	1500	75	5	-5	70
Dave	1300	65	8	-8	57
Sam	1900	95	11	-11	**84**

Question No.	Answer Key	Detailed Explanation
5	C	Since the y-intercept occurs at (0, 6) we know that it has to be answer choice A or C because the c value in standard form $ax^2 + bx + c$ is the y-intercept. Therefore the equation must have a+6 at the end. You can use the x-intercepts and work backwards to find the rest of the equation. Since the zeros are -2 and -3, we can write factors (x+2)(x+3). Now use the FOIL method and multiply those together and arrive at $x^2 + 5x + 6$ which is answer choice C.

Lesson 7: Calculating and Interpreting Rate of Change

Question No.	Answer Key	Detailed Explanation
1	A	We need to see how much the rain increased in inches and divide that by the number of days after Tuesday until you reach Friday as shown below. $\frac{10-3}{3}=\frac{7}{3}=2.33=2\frac{1}{3}$ inches per day.
2	C	To find the rate of change of speed (a), find the change in speed and divide it by the time interval during which the speed changed. But the speed is given in miles per hour and the duration is 7 seconds. Therefore, change seconds into hours. 7 seconds $=\dfrac{7}{3600}$ hours $a=\dfrac{60-20}{\frac{7}{3600}}$ $a=20571.43$ miles/s^2
3	B	First we need to find f(5) and f(3). $f(5)=3(5)^2+7(5)-16=94$ $f(3)=3(3)^2+7(3)-16=32$ Next we need to calculate the change in f(x) divided by the change in x as shown below $\dfrac{\Delta f(x)}{\Delta x}=\dfrac{94-32}{5-3}=\dfrac{62}{2}=31$
4	D	First we need to find g(−1) and g(5). $g(-1)=\dfrac{1}{2(-1)}-(-1)^2=-1.5$ $g(5)=\dfrac{1}{2(5)}-(5)^2=-24.9$ Next we need to calculate the change in g(x) divided by the change in x as shown below $\dfrac{\Delta g(x)}{\Delta x}=\dfrac{-24.9-(-1.5)}{5-(-1)}=\dfrac{-23.4}{6}=-3.9$

Question No.	Answer Key	Detailed Explanation
5	A	The function value at s=4 is 4. The function value at s=10 is 20. Now calculate the change in m/s over the change in s. $$\frac{\Delta m/s}{\Delta s} = \frac{20\text{-}4}{10\text{-}4} = \frac{16}{6} = 2.66 = 2\frac{2}{3}$$

Lesson 8: Understanding the Graph of a Function

Question No.	Answer Key	Detailed Explanation
1	C	A function is positive when its graph is above the x-axis. Notice in the graph that the function's graph is above the x-axis in the interval $(-3,2) \cup (5,\infty)$ and below the x-axis on the interval $(-\infty,-3) \cup (2,5)$.
2	B	The parent square root curve has its beginning on the origin which is the point $(0,0)$ and has the equation $y=\sqrt{x}$. The graph in the figure has its beginning on the point $(3,1)$. This means the parent function is moved 3 units to the right and 1 unit upward, giving a new equation: $y=\sqrt{x-3}+1$.
3	B	A function has a zero when the graph of the function touches or crosses the x-axis. Notice that the graph crosses the x-axis at $x=-3,-1,1,3$ which means the function has 4 zeros.
4	B	A polynomial function always has one fewer turning points that the degree of the function. The question states that the graph is that of a quintic polynomial, which is a 5th degree polynomial. Therefore, the graph would automatically have one less than five turning points, or four.
5	C	The parent cube root curve has its vertical point on the origin which is the point $(0,0)$ and has the equation $y=\sqrt[3]{x}$. The graph in the figure has its vertical point on the point $(-2,-3)$. This means the parent function is moved 2 units to the left and 3 unit downward, giving a new equation: $y=\sqrt[3]{x+2}-3$.

Question No.	Answer Key	Detailed Explanation
1	A	This problem can be easily solved using the quadratic formula as shown below. $$x = \frac{-(-7)\pm\sqrt{(-7)^2 - 4(5)(1)}}{2(5)}$$ $$x = \frac{7\pm\sqrt{29}}{10}$$ This cannot be reduced anymore so this is the final answer.
2	C	Since the velocity is increasing we need to add the 3 directly to the v. The only one that does that is answer choice C.
3	B	Since the base i.e. $1.06 > 1$, it indicates growth. The .06 in the equation would be the percent growth written as a decimal. To change the decimal back to a percent, move the decimal two places to the right making it 6%
4	C	To find the value at the maximum, you can use the formula $x = -\frac{b}{2a}$. In this case x would be t. $$t = \frac{-b}{2a} = \frac{-5}{2(-4)} = \frac{5}{8}$$
5		You need to factor to find the x-intercepts (the places where $y = 0$) for this function. $y = 6x^2 + 2x$ $y = 2x(3x + 1)$ Now set each factor equal to zero and solve. $2x = 0$ and $3x + 1 = 0$ $x = 0$ and $x = -\frac{1}{3}$

Lesson 10: Comparing Properties of Functions

Question No.	Answer Key	Detailed Explanation
1	C	We can tell that the slope of Line a is 3, because when an equation is in slope-intercept form ($y = mx + b$), the slope is the m or the number beside x. We can calculate the slope for line b using the slope formula $m=\frac{y_2-y_1}{x_2-x_1}$. $m=\frac{3-1}{3-0}=\frac{2}{3}$ Since 3 is bigger than $\frac{2}{3}$, we can say that Line a has the greater slope.
2	A	While it appears that they both have y-values that reach -4, the parabola is the only one that actually touches -4. The exponential function has a horizontal asymptote at y=-4, meaning it never actually reaches that value.
3	D	Vertical asymptotes happen whenever the Denominator equals zero. Since we have two rational equations we will have to find the asymptotes for each to list them all. denominator of f(x): $x+2=0$, so $x=-2$ denominator of g(x): $x^2-4=0$, so $(x+2)(x-2)=0$, so $x=-2$ and $x=2$
4	B	Number of zeros of a function ≤ Order of the function. Since the order of f(x) is 3, there can be maximum 3 zeros for that function. The order of g(x) would be 5 because there are 5 separate x's that would be multiplied together making an x^5 in the simplified function. So g(x) would have more zeros.
5	D	We know that f(x) has an order of 6, which means the highest power in the equation is a 6. We also know that f(x) crosses the y-axis at -1. Since this is a u-shaped graph, we know it will cross the x-axis twice. A linear function with an undefined slope is a straight vertical line and will only touch the x-axis once.

Lesson 11: Construct Linear and Exponential Functions

Question No.	Answer Key	Detailed Explanation
1	C	The graph shows that the function is an exponential growth function. The formula for an exponential function is $f(x)=ab^x$, where a is the y-intercept and b is the growth factor. If the exponential function is a growth function, then $b>1$. If the exponential function is a decay function, then $0<b<1$. The graph shows that the y-intercept is (0, 3), so $a=3$. The graph passes through the point (-1,2). We can find b by substituting $x = -1$ and $y = 2$ in $y = 3b^x$. $2=3 \times b^{-1}$ $2=3/b$ $b = 1.5$. Thus, the function whose graph is shown in the question is $f(x)=3(1.5)^x$.
2	A	The values in the table do not reflect a linear relationship because the y-values are increasing at an increasing rate. They also do not reflect an exponential relationship because each y-value is not the previous y-value multiplied by a specific value number. A close look at the relationship between the x- and y- values reveals that the points are all in the form (x,x^2), so the function whose values are in the table is $f(x)=x^2$.
3	B	The graph shows that the function is an exponential function. The formula for an exponential function is $f(x)=ab^x$, where a is the y-intercept and b is the growth factor. If the exponential function is a growth function, then $b>1$. If the exponential function is a decay function, then $0<b<1$. The graph passes through the points (0,5) and (1,2) which are one unit apart on the x-axis, so find b by dividing $2 \div 5$, $b=0.4$. The function whose graph is shown in the question is $f(x)=5(0.4)^x$.
4	A	The table shows that the y-values always decrease by 4. Therefore the function is a linear relationship between the input and the output variables with a slope of -4. The question does not provide the y-intercept, so use the point-slope form of a linear equation. The formula is $y-y_1=m(x-x_1)$, where y_1 is the y-value in a specific point and x_1 is the x-value in the same point, and m is the slope. Use the point $(1,-4)$ to find the equation of the line from the table. Now you have $y-(-4)=-4(x-1)$, which simplifies to $y+4=-4x+4$ and $y=-4x$. Change the equation to function notation and the function is $f(x)=-4x$.

Question No.	Answer Key	Detailed Explanation
5	A	The graph shows a linear function, so the formula, in slope-intercept form is $f(x)=mx+b$, where m is the slope of the line (rise over run) and b is the y-intercept. Looking at the graph, select the two points $(0,-3)$ and $(4,0)$ to calculate the slope. The formula and calculations are: $m=\dfrac{y_2-y_1}{x_2-x_1}=\dfrac{0-(-3)}{4-0}=\dfrac{3}{4}$. The graph shows that the y-intercept is $(0,-3)$, so $b=-3$. The function whose graph is shown is $f(x)=\dfrac{3}{4}x-3$.

Question No.	Answer Key	Detailed Explanation
1	C	The number of sheets of sheetrock the company has on hand is the result of adding the deliveries of sheetrock to the inventory of sheetrock on hand. The problem says the company has 550 sheets of sheetrock on hand so the beginning inventory is 550. The deliveries is the number of sheets of sheetrock on each truckload times the number of trucks. Each truck holds 75 sheets and there are t truckloads, so the total deliveries is 75t. Therefore, the function that represents the inventory is P(t)=75t+550.
2	A	The number of hamburger buns in the store room is calculated by subtracting the number of hamburgers sold from the initial inventory of hamburger buns. The problem states that the restaurant has 750 hamburger buns at the beginning of the week. The number of hamburgers sold is calculated by multiplying the sales per day by the number of days. The problem also states that the restaurant business expects to sell 250 hamburgers every day and the variable b represents the number of days. Therefore, the function that represents the number of hamburger buns in the store room after b days is H(b)=750-250b.
3	B	The number of students at the school is calculated by adding the number of students who were at the school in the beginning to the number of new students. The problem states that the school started with 64 students. The number of additional students is calculated by multiplying the number of new students per year by the number of years. The problem also states that the school expects to enroll 26 students every year and the variable x represents the number of years. Therefore, the function that represents the number of students at the school after x years is S(x)=64+26x.
4	B	The number of diplomas that have been presented is calculated by adding the number of diplomas that have already been presented to the diplomas being presented each hour times the number of hours. The problem states that the dean has already presented 56 diplomas. The number of diplomas being presented is calculated by multiplying the diplomas per minute (times 60 to determine the number of diplomas per hour) times the number of hours. The problem also states that the dean can present 5 diplomas per minute or 300 diplomas per hour, and the variable h represents the number of hours. Therefore, the function that represents the number of diplomas presented after h hours is D(h)=56+300h.

Question No.	Answer Key	Detailed Explanation
5	50	The problem says that a fundraising company had 2,500 notebooks for a fund drive telethon and they have already given away 750 of them during a pre fund drive event. The sponsors expect to give-away 85 notebooks per hour during the fund drive. You are asked to determine how many notebooks will be left after the telethon, which will be20 hours long. Write a function that subtracts the number of early giveaways from the original number of notebooks and then subtracts 85 notebooks per hour. Use the variable n for the number of hours. The function that represents the number of notebooks remaining after n hours is $H(n)=2500-750-85n$. Now, evaluate the function for $n=20$. $H(20)=2500-750-85(20)=50$. The sponsors can expect to have 50 notebooks remaining.

Lesson 13: Exponential Models Expressed as Logarithms

Question No.	Answer Key	Detailed Explanation
1	C	The definition of the natural log (shortened to "ln") is $\log_e$, so when you see e as the base of an exponent, always think natural log.
2	B	Solve as shown $e^{3x}=27$ $3x=\ln 27$ $x=\dfrac{\ln 27}{3}$
3	C	You could convert into either A or B and solve using the calculator using logarithmic rules.
4	A	Covert as shown below $5e^x=120$ $e^x=24$ $x=\ln 24$
5	B	Covert as shown below $3e^x=33$ $e^x=11$ $x=\ln 11$

Lesson 14: Radians, Degrees, and Arc Length

Question No.	Answer Key	Detailed Explanation
1	B	In radians, π is equivalent to 180° . Therefore, we can write a multiplier to convert between radians and degrees without changing the value of the angle. The multiplier to convert from radians to degrees is $\dfrac{180°}{\pi}$ and the multiplier to convert from degrees to radians is $\dfrac{\pi}{180°}$. Both of these multipliers are equal to 1. To convert from $\dfrac{2\pi}{3}$ radians to degrees, the π in the angle measure must be eliminated. Therefore, we multiply the radian measure by $\dfrac{180°}{\pi}$. The calculations are $\dfrac{2\pi}{3} \times \dfrac{180°}{\pi} = \dfrac{2 \times 180°}{3} = 120°$.
2	D	Length of an arc can be calculated using the formula l=r*θ where l is the length of the arc; r is the radius and θ is the angle subtended by the arc at the center in radians. $l = \dfrac{15 * 36 * \pi}{180}$ $l = 3\pi$
3	C	Length of an arc can be calculated using the formula l=r*θ where l is the length of the arc; r is the radius and θ is the angle subtended by the arc at the center in radians. $l = \dfrac{14 * 2\pi}{7}$ $l = 4\pi$
4	C	In radians, π is equivalent to 180°. Therefore, we can write a multiplier to convert between radians and degrees without changing the value of the angle. The multiplier to convert from radians to degrees is $\dfrac{180°}{\pi}$ and the multiplier to convert from degrees to radians is $\dfrac{\pi}{180°}$. Both of these multipliers are equal to 1. To convert from 55° to radians, the degrees in the angle measure must be eliminated. Therefore, we multiply the radian measure by $\dfrac{\pi}{180°}$. The calculations are $55° \times \dfrac{\pi}{180°} = \dfrac{55° \times \pi}{180°} = \dfrac{11\pi}{36}$.

Question No.	Answer Key	Detailed Explanation
5	D	In radians, π is equivalent to $180°$. Therefore, we can write a multiplier to convert between radians and degrees without changing the value of the angle. The multiplier to convert from radians to degrees is $\frac{180°}{\pi}$ and the multiplier to convert from degrees to radians is $\frac{\pi}{180°}$. Both of these multipliers are equal to 1. To convert from $\frac{4\pi}{9}$ radians to degrees, the π in the angle measure must be eliminated. Therefore, we multiply the radian measure by $\frac{180°}{\pi}$. The calculations are $\frac{4\pi}{9} \times \frac{180°}{\pi} = \frac{4 \times 180°}{9} = 80°$.

Question No.	Answer Key	Detailed Explanation
1	D	Plot the point (-3,-4) in Quadrant III of the coordinate plane. Find the value of the hypotenuse of the triangle formed using the point and the x-axis. Since $c^2=a^2+b^2$, the hypotenuse will be 5. Now use the ratio for sin, $\sin O = \frac{y}{r} = \frac{\text{opposite}}{\text{hypotenuse}}$. So, $\sin O = \frac{-4}{5}$.
2	B	Plot the point (5, 12) in Quadrant I of the coordinate plane. Find the value of the hypotenuse of the triangle formed using the point and the x-axis. Since $c^2=a^2+b^2$, the hypotenuse will be 13. Now use the ratio for tan, $\tan O = \frac{y}{x} = \frac{\text{opposite}}{\text{adjacent}}$, $x\neq0$. So, $\sin O = \frac{12}{5}$.
3	C	Since $\frac{4\pi}{3}$ is located in Quadrant III, the sign of cosine will be negative. Also, since $\frac{4\pi}{3}$ has a $\frac{\pi}{3}$ reference angle, that the cosine will be the same as the $\cos\frac{\pi}{3}$, just negative since it is in Quadrant III. The $\cos\frac{\pi}{3} = \frac{1}{2}$, so $\cos\frac{4\pi}{3}$ will have to be $-\frac{1}{2}$.
4	B	Since $\frac{5\pi}{6}$ is located in Quadrant II, the sign of cosecant will be positive. Also, since $\frac{5\pi}{6}$ has a $\frac{\pi}{6}$ reference angle, that the cosecant will be the same as the cosecant of $\frac{\pi}{6}$. The $\sin\frac{\pi}{6}$ is $\frac{1}{2}$. Since cosecant is the reciprocal of sine, $\csc\frac{\pi}{6}=2$.
5	B	(3, 2) is located in Quadrant I in which all trig functions are positive. Locate the point in the coordinate plane and locate the sides of the triangle formed with the x-axis and the terminal side. The horizontal distance will be 3 and the vertical distance will be 2. Then use Pythagorean Theorem to find the hypotenuse. $c^2=a^2+b^2$. So $c^2=3^2+2^2$; therefore, $c=\sqrt{13}$. The trig ratio for cosecant $\csc O = \frac{y}{r} = \frac{\text{opposite}}{\text{hypotenuse}}$, $y\neq0$. So the answer is B.

Question No.	Answer Key	Detailed Explanation
1	C	The sine function $y=\sin x$, the parent function, has a period of 2π. The function $y=a \sin (bx+c)$ has a period of $\frac{2\pi}{b}$. In the function $y=2 \sin (\frac{3x}{4})-5$, $b=34$. Therefore, the period of this function is $\frac{2\pi}{\frac{3}{4}}$ which is simplified by $\frac{2\pi}{1} \times \frac{4}{3} = \frac{8\pi}{3}$.
2	A	The amplitude of the function $y=\sin x$ or $y=\cos x$ is 1 because the maximum value of this periodic function is 1, the minimum value is -1, and the midline equation is $y=0$. The amplitude is the vertical distance between the midline and the maximum or the minimum, which is 1. The trigonometric function in this problem is $y=-2\sin(x-\pi)+3$ which is a vertical stretch of the parent function by a factor of 2 , a reflection across the x-axis, and an upward shift of 3 units. However, the vertical shift does not affect the amplitude. Therefore, the maximum value of this periodic function is 5, the minimum value is 1, and the midline equation is $y=3$. The amplitude is 2.
3	C	The function $y=\cos x$, the parent function, has a period of 2π. The function $y=a \cos (bx+c)$ has a period of $\frac{2\pi}{b}$. In the function $y=-4\cos (\frac{2\pi x}{5})$, $b=\frac{2\pi}{5}$. Therefore, the period of this function is $\frac{2\pi}{\frac{2\pi}{5}}$ which is simplified by $\frac{2\pi}{1} \times \frac{5}{2\pi} = 5$.
4	B	The sine function $y=\sin x$, the parent function, has a period of 2π. The function $y=a \sin (bx+c)$ has a period of $\frac{2\pi}{b}$. In the function $y=-3 \sin (\frac{2x}{7})+6$, $b=27$. Therefore, the period of this function is $\frac{2\pi}{\frac{2}{7}}$ which is simplified by $\frac{2\pi}{1} \times \frac{7}{2} = 7\pi$.
5	C	The sine function $y=\sin x$, the parent function, has a period of 2π. The function $y=a \sin (bx+c)$ has a period of $\frac{2\pi}{b}$. In the function $y=-3 \sin (2x)+1$. Therefore, the period of this function is $\frac{2\pi}{2}$ which is simplified by $\frac{2\pi}{1} \times \frac{1}{2} = \pi$.

Question No.	Answer Key	Detailed Explanation
1	D	To find the answer, use the Pythagorean Identity, substitute, and solve for cos θ.

$$\sin^2\theta + \cos^2\theta = 1; \quad (-\frac{6}{10})^2 + \cos^2\theta = 1; \quad \frac{36}{100} + \cos^2\theta = 1$$

$$\cos^2\theta = \frac{64}{100}; \quad \sqrt{\cos^2\theta} = \pm\sqrt{\frac{64}{100}}; \quad \cos\theta = \pm\frac{8}{10}$$

Next, use the fact that θ is in quadrant IV, and the signs of the trigonometric functions change in each quadrant. The figure below shows when the signs of the trigonometric functions' signs are positive. The co-function of each has the same sign. All other trigonometric functions are negative in those quadrants.

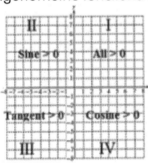

Since θ is in quadrant IV, cos θ>0, and tan θ<0. Thus, since $\tan\theta = \frac{\sin\theta}{\cos\theta}$,

$$\tan\theta = -\frac{-\frac{6}{10}}{\frac{8}{10}} = -\frac{6}{8} = -\frac{3}{4}.$$

| 2 | C | To find the answer, use the Pythagorean Identity, substitute, and solve for sin θ. |

$$\sin^2\theta + \cos^2\theta = 1; \quad \sin^2\theta + (-\frac{15}{17})^2 = 1; \quad \sin^2\theta + \frac{225}{289} = 1$$

$$\sin^2\theta = \frac{64}{289}; \quad \sqrt{\cos^2\theta} = \pm\sqrt{\frac{64}{289}}; \quad \sin\theta = \pm\frac{8}{17}$$

Next, use the fact that θ is in quadrant III, and the signs of the trigonometric functions change in each quadrant. The figure below shows when the signs of the trigonometric functions' signs are positive. The co-function of each has the same sign. All other trigonometric functions are negative in those quadrants.

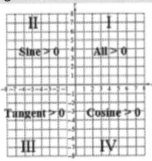

Since θ is in quadrant III, sin θ<0. Therefore, $\sin\theta = -\frac{8}{17}$.

Question No.	Answer Key	Detailed Explanation
3	A	

To find the answer, use the Pythagorean Identity, substitute, and solve for $\sin \theta$.

$$\sin^2\theta + \cos^2\theta = 1; \quad \sin^2\theta + (\frac{5}{13})^2 = 1; \quad \sin^2\theta + \frac{25}{169} = 1$$

$$\sin^2\theta = \frac{144}{169}; \quad \sqrt{\sin^2\theta} = \pm\sqrt{\frac{144}{169}}; \quad \sin\theta = \pm\frac{12}{13}$$

Next, use the fact that θ is in quadrant IV, and the signs of the trigonometric functions change in each quadrant. The figure below shows when the signs of the trigonometric functions' signs are positive. The co-function of each has the same sign. All other trigonometric functions are negative in those quadrants.

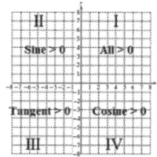

Since θ is in quadrant IV, $\sin \theta < 0$, so $\tan \theta < 0$. Thus, since Therefore, $\tan\theta = \frac{\sin\theta}{\cos\theta}$,

$$\tan\theta = -\frac{-\frac{12}{13}}{\frac{5}{13}} = -\frac{12}{5}.$$

| 4 | B | |

To find the answer, use the Pythagorean Identity, substitute, and solve for $\cos \theta$.

$$\sin^2\theta + \cos^2\theta = 1; \quad (\frac{24}{25})^2 + \cos^2\theta = 1; \quad \frac{576}{625} + \cos^2\theta = 1$$

$$\cos^2\theta = \frac{49}{625}; \quad \sqrt{\cos^2\theta} = \pm\sqrt{\frac{49}{625}}; \quad \cos\theta = \pm\frac{7}{25}$$

Next, use the fact that θ is in quadrant III, and the signs of the trigonometric functions change in each quadrant. The figure below shows when the signs of the trigonometric functions' signs are positive. The co-function of each has the same sign. All other trigonometric functions are negative in those quadrants.

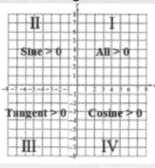

Since θ is in quadrant III, $\cos \theta < 0$.

Therefore, $\cos\theta = -\frac{7}{25}$.

Question No.	Answer Key	Detailed Explanation
5	C	

To find the answer, use the Pythagorean Identity, substitute, and solve for cos θ.

$$\sin^2\theta + \cos^2\theta = 1; \left(\frac{4}{5}\right)^2 + \cos^2\theta = 1; \frac{16}{25} + \cos^2\theta = 1$$

$$\cos^2\theta = \frac{9}{25}; \sqrt{\cos^2\theta} = \pm\sqrt{\frac{9}{25}}; \cos\theta = \pm\frac{3}{5}$$

Next, use the fact that θ iis in quadrant II, and the signs of the trigonometric functions change in each quadrant. The figure below shows when the signs of the trigonometric functions' signs are positive. The co-function of each has the same sign. All other trigonometric functions are negative in those quadrants.

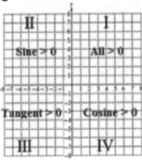

Since θ is in quadrant II, cos θ<0.

Therefore, $\cos\theta = -\frac{3}{5}$.

Answer Key
&
Detailed Explanations

Chapter 4:
Number and Quantity

Question No.	Answer Key	Detailed Explanation
1	D	$(2+4i)(1-i) = 2-2i+4i-4i^2 = 2+2i+4 = 6+2i$ Use the FOIL method for multiplying two binomials together. Simplify by combining the two middle terms $2i+4i$ since they are like terms. Next simplify $-4i^2$ to be $-4 \times -1 = 4$, since $i^2 = -1$ by definition. Finally we can add the 4 and 2 together to get the answer $6+2i$.
2	A	$(2-3i)^2 = 2^2 + (3i)^2 - 2 \times 2 \times 3i$ (Using the identity $(a-b)^2 = a^2+b^2-2ab$) $= 4 + 9i^2 - 12i$ $= 4 - 9 - 12i$ (Since $i^2 = -1$) $= -5 - 12i$
3	B	$i(7-i) = i \times 7 - i \times i = 7i - i^2 = 7i-(-1) = 7i+1 = 1+7i$ Start by using the distributive method. Now simplify $-i^2 = 1$ by definition. Now rearrange and put the real part first and the imaginary part last so that it looks like this $a+bi$.
4	C	$6i(4i-3) = 6i \times 4i - 6i \times 3 = 24i^2 - 18i = 24 \times -1 - 18i = -24-18i$ Start by distributing. Make sure and multiply by the $6i$. Now simplify $24i^2$ since $i^2 = -1$ by definition we have $24 \times -1 = -24$. So the final answer is $-24-18i$.
5	D	$(4+3i)(4-3i) = 16-12i+12i-9i^2 = 16-9(-1) = 16+9 = 25$ Use the FOIL method for multiplying two binomials. When you combine the like terms $-12i+12i$ they eliminate each other leaving only $16-9i^2$. Then you simplify the $-9i^2$ by using the fact that $i^2 = -1$ by definition. This leaves $16+9$ which is 25.

Lesson 2: Introduction to Imaginary and Complex Numbers

Question No.	Answer Key	Detailed Explanation
1	D	This problem has a real part (3) and an imaginary part (7i). You cannot add real and imaginary numbers together since they are not like terms. You can only add/subtract real numbers with other real numbers. Likewise you can only add/subtract imaginary numbers with other imaginary numbers. Therefore the answer looks just like the problem.
2	D	Since an imaginary number is defined as $i=\sqrt{-1}$, we should be able to square both sides of that equation and get a value for i^2 like so, $(i)^2=(\sqrt{-1})^2$. That simplifies to i^2 on the left and -1 on the right. A square root and a square are opposite operations so they basically delete each other and the -1 comes out as is.
3	C	There are real and imaginary parts of the problem 2+6+4i. The real parts are the 2 and 6. Those two parts can be added together to make 8. The 4i is the only imaginary part so it must stay as is and cannot combine with any of the real parts in this problem. The resulting answer is 8+4i.
4	D	We can use the multiplying radicals rule to help us simplify this radical. Our answer should be imaginary since you can't really take the square root of a negative number. We split the radical in two parts $\sqrt{-1} \times \sqrt{81}$. We know that $\sqrt{-1}=i$ and 81 is a perfect square whose square root is 9. Therefore our simplified answer is 9i.
5	B	This problem consists of two perfect square numbers under radicals. This means your final answer should not have a radical at all. The first radical listed $\sqrt{36}=6$ so it's a real number. The second radical in the problem simplifies to 2i as follows $\sqrt{-4}=\sqrt{4} \times \sqrt{-1}=2i$. So this part is imaginary. So we have 6+2i. You cannot combine these two terms because one part is real and one part is imaginary.

Question No.	Answer Key	Detailed Explanation
1	B	We solve quadratic equations in the form $ax^2+bx+c=0$ by factoring, completing the squares, or with the quadratic formula. The question asks us to solve the equation $x^2+4x+22=13$. The first step is to set the equation equal zero by subtracting 13 from both sides. The new equation is: $x^2+4x+9=0$. Now, we will solve using the quadratic formula, $x=\dfrac{-b\pm\sqrt{b^2-4ac}}{2a}$, which gives us $x=\dfrac{-4\pm\sqrt{16-4(1)(9)}}{2(1)}=\dfrac{-4\pm\sqrt{-20}}{2}=\dfrac{-4\pm2i\sqrt{5}}{2}=-2\pm i\sqrt{5}$. The solution to the equation is $x=-2\pm i\sqrt{5}$.
2	B	We solve quadratic equations in the form $ax^2+bx+c=0$ by factoring, completing the squares, using the square root method, or with the quadratic formula. The question asks us to solve the equation $-5x^2-52=3$. We will solve using the square root method. First, we will add 52 to both sides. The new equation is: $-5x^2=55$. Now, we will solve by dividing by -5 and square rooting, which gives us $-5x^2=55$, $x^2=-11$, $\sqrt{x^2}=\pm\sqrt{-11}$, $x=\pm i\sqrt{11}$. The solution to the equation is $x=\pm i\sqrt{11}$.
3	D	We solve quadratic equations in the form $ax^2+bx+c=0$ by factoring, completing the squares, or with the quadratic formula. The question asks us to solve the equation $x^2+4x=-5$. The first step is to set the equation equal zero by adding 5 on both the sides. The new equation is: $x^2+4x+5=0$. Now, we will solve using the quadratic formula, $x=\dfrac{-b\pm\sqrt{b^2-4ac}}{2a}$, which gives us $x=\dfrac{-4\pm\sqrt{16-4(1)(5)}}{2(1)}=\dfrac{-4\pm\sqrt{-4}}{2}=\dfrac{-4\pm2i}{2}=-2\pm i$. The solution to the equation is $x=-2\pm i$.
4	C	We solve quadratic equations in the form $ax^2+bx+c=0$ by factoring, completing the squares, or with the quadratic formula. The question asks us to solve the equation $-3x^2-9x-12=0$. The first step is to reduce the equation by dividing by -3. The new equation is: $x^2+3x+4=0$. Now, we will solve using the quadratic formula, $x=\dfrac{-b\pm\sqrt{b^2-4ac}}{2a}$, which gives us $x=\dfrac{-3\pm\sqrt{9-4(1)(4)}}{2(-1)}=\dfrac{-3\pm i\sqrt{-7}}{2}=\dfrac{-3\pm i\sqrt{7}}{2}$. The solution to the equation is $x=\dfrac{-3\pm i\sqrt{7}}{2}$.

Question No.	Answer Key	Detailed Explanation
5	B	We solve quadratic equations in the form $ax^2+bx+c=0$ by factoring, completing the squares, or with the quadratic formula. The question asks us to solve the equation $-2x^2-5x-2=4$. The first step is to set the equation equal zero by subtracting 4 from both sides. The new equation is: $-2x^2-5x-6=0$. Now, we will solve using the quadratic formula, $x=\dfrac{-b\pm\sqrt{b^2-4ac}}{2a}$, which gives us $x=\dfrac{5\pm\sqrt{25-4(-2)(-6)}}{2(-2)}=\dfrac{5\pm\sqrt{-23}}{-4}=\dfrac{-5\pm i\sqrt{23}}{4}$. The solution to the equation is $x=\dfrac{-5\pm i\sqrt{23}}{4}$.

Question No.	Answer Key	Detailed Explanation
1	C	Jenna has $100 to spend. She should buy one 10 pound package for $60 and two 3 pound packages for $20 each. This gives her 16 pounds of cookies.
2	C	In order to buy exactly 10 kg of corn or rice, you must purchase two 2 kg packages of corn for $15 each and two 3 kg packages of rice for $20. The calculations are 2(2)kg+2(3)kg = 10kg and 2(15)+2(20) = 70.
3	D	To calculate the total cost, determine how many of each length he would need. Then multiply that number by the price for that length. 10 feet— 17; 360 ÷ 10=36; 36 × 17= $612 12 feet— 23; 360 ÷ 12=30; 30 × 23= $690 20 feet— 34; 360 ÷ 20=18; 18 × 34= $612 30 feet— 45; 360 ÷ 30=12; 12 × 45= $540
4	A	Since the coffee pool pays $39.60 for a case of 120 k-cup pods, each pod costs $0.33. Juanita says she drinks 3 cups per day, five days each week, for 49 weeks per year. Multiply these numbers, 3 × 5 × 49=735 to get the number of cups she drinks per year. Now, multiply that quantity by the price per cup: 735 × 0.33 = 242.55
5	37 kg	Small → 2 kg for $6 → unit price is $3 per kg; Medium → 5 kg for $8 → unit price is $1.60 per kg; and Large → 15 kg for $18 → unit price is 1.20 per kg. Next, purchase as many large packets as possible, which is 2 packets for $36. They have $14 left. Now, purchase as many medium packets as possible, which is 1 packet for $8. Now, they have $6, which is enough for one small packet. Add the kg purchased: 2(15)+5+2=37.

Lesson 5: Evaluating Rational Exponents

Question No.	Answer Key	Detailed Explanation
1	B	The question asks for an equivalent radical expression for $16^{\frac{5}{4}}$. A rational exponent can be rewritten using radicals because the denominator of the exponent is a root. Thus $16^{\frac{1}{4}}=\sqrt[4]{16}$ and $\sqrt[4]{16}=2$. Therefore, the number expression $16^{\frac{5}{4}}=(\sqrt[4]{16})^5=2^5=32$.
2	C	The question asks for an equivalent simplified radical expression for $9^{\frac{2}{5}}$. A rational exponent can be rewritten using radicals because the denominator of the exponent is a root. Thus $9^{\frac{1}{5}}=\sqrt[5]{9}$. Then the radical expression is raised to the power of the numerator of the original rational exponent. Therefore, the number expression $9^{\frac{2}{5}}=(\sqrt[5]{9})^2$ or $\sqrt[5]{9^2}$.
3	C	The question asks for an equivalent expression with a rational exponent for $(\sqrt[4]{17})^3$. A radical expression can be rewritten using rational exponents because the root of the radical is the denominator of the exponent. Thus $\sqrt[4]{17}=17^{\frac{1}{4}}$ and $(\sqrt[4]{17})^3$ means cubing the expression. Therefore, the radical expression $(\sqrt[4]{17})^3=(17^{\frac{1}{4}})^3$. Next, use the exponent rule commonly referred to as the power of another power. This rule states that you multiply the powers. Therefore, the final expression is $17^{\frac{3}{4}}$.
4	B	The question asks for an equivalent radical expression for $18^{\frac{2}{5}}$. A rational exponent can be rewritten using radicals because the denominator of the exponent is a root. Thus $18^{\frac{1}{5}}=\sqrt[5]{18}$. Then the radical expression is raised to the power of the numerator of the original rational exponent. Therefore, the number expression $18^{\frac{2}{5}}=(\sqrt[5]{18})^2$ or $\sqrt[5]{18^2}$.
5	B	The question asks for an equivalent expression for $(125^{\frac{3}{2}})^{\frac{4}{9}}$. First, use the exponent rule commonly referred to as the power of another power rule. This rule says to multiply the exponent in the given expression. Therefore, $(125^{\frac{3}{2}})^{\frac{4}{9}}=(125)^{\frac{3}{2}\times\frac{4}{9}}=(125)^{\frac{2}{3}}$. A rational exponent can be rewritten using radicals because the denominator of the exponent is a root. Thus $125^{\frac{1}{3}}=\sqrt[3]{125}$ and $\sqrt[3]{125}=5$. Next, the numerator in the exponent means that you raise the base to that power. Therefore, the number expression $(125^{\frac{3}{2}})^{\frac{4}{9}}=5^2=25$.

Question No.	Answer Key	Detailed Explanation
1	5	In a problem with a rational exponent, the numerator tells you the power, and the denominator the root. Since $\sqrt[5]{625}$ is taking a 5th root, the missing denominator would be 5.
2	C	In a problem with a rational exponent, the numerator tells you the power, and the denominator the root. Since we are taking a cube root to the first power in the problem $\sqrt[3]{125}$, the exponent should be $\frac{1}{3}$. So the correct answer is $125^{\frac{1}{3}}$.
3	A	In a problem with a rational exponent, the numerator tells you the power, and the denominator the root. Since the problem is, $x^{\frac{1}{2}}$, the denominator is 2 indicating we should take a square root and the numerator is 1 so we would raise that to the first power or there will be no exponent since an exponent of 1 is rarely used. That makes the answer the square root of x, written as $\sqrt{x}$.
4	B	In a problem with a rational exponent, the numerator tells you the power, and the denominator the root. In the problem, $27^{\frac{2}{3}}$, the denominator is 3 indicating we should take the cube root of 27. The numerator is 2 which means we should square either before or after we take the cube root. So there are two possible correct answers to this problem. One is answer choice B. The other would be $\sqrt[3]{27^2}$.
5	D	Problems written in radical form can be written in exponential form using the rational exponent rule. In the problem, $\sqrt[5]{x^2}$, the root is 5 indicating denominator of the rational exponent would be 5. The power is 2 indicating the numerator of the rational exponent would be 2. So the correct answer would be x to the $\frac{2}{5}$ power.

Algebra 2 FAQs

What will Algebra 2 Assessment Look Like?

In many ways, the Algebra 2 assessments will be unlike anything many students have ever seen. The tests require students to complete tasks to assess a deeper understanding of Algebra 2.

Is it necessary to take the Algebra 1 before taking up Algebra 2?

The students can decide their preferred High School credit program based on their future college graduation choices. However, it is recommended to take either Algebra 1 or Integrated Math 1 and Geometry first before choosing Algebra 2 as this helps the students to master the basic skills.

What are the Math credit programs offered in High Schools?

Most of the High Schools offer Algebra 1, Algebra 2, Geometry, Integrated Math 1 and Integrated Math 2.

What item types are included in the Online Algebra 2 Test?

Because the assessment is online, the test will consist of a combination of new types of questions:

1. Drag and Drop
2. Drop Down
3. Essay Response
4. Extended Constructed Response
5. Hot Text Select and Drag
6. Hot Text Selective Highlight
7. Matching Table In-line
8. Matching Table Single Response
9. Multiple Choice – Single Correct Response, radial buttons
10. Multiple Choice – Multiple Response, checkboxes
11. Numeric Response
12. Short Text
13. Table Fill-in

Step 1 → **Visit the link given below and login to your parent/teacher account**
www.lumoslearning.com

Step 2 → Go to the **"My tedBooks"** section and place the book access code and submit
(See the first page for access code).

Step 3 → **Add the new book**

To add the new book for a registered student, choose the '**Student**' button and
click on submit.

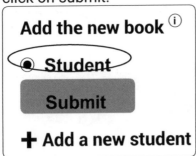

To add the new book for a new student, choose the '**Add New Student**' button
and complete the student registration.

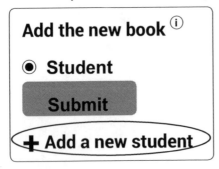

Progress Chart

Lesson	Q No.	Page No.	Practice		Mastered	Re-practice /Reteach
			Date	Score		
Chapter 2: Algebra		8				
Remainder Theorem & Zeros of a Polynomial		9				
Binomial Theorem		11				
Rewrite Simple Rational Expressions		12				
Create Equations And Inequalities In One Variable		14				
Explaining Equation and using properties		16				
Solve Linear Equations and Inequalities with One Variable		17				
Solve Quadratic Equations with One Variable		18				
Solving Systems of Equations in Two Variables		19				
Solve Systems of Equations Exactly and Approximately		20				
Reasoning with Equations and Graphs		22				
Solve simple rational and radical equations in one variable		23				
Solve a simple system consisting of a linear equation and a quadratic equation		24				
Interpret parts of an Expression		26				
Rewriting Expressions		27				
Writing Expressions in Equivalent Forms		28				
Finding the sum of a Finite Geometric Series		29				

Lesson	Q No.	Page No.	Practice		Mastered	Re-practice /Reteach
			Date	Score		
Chapter 4: Number and Quantity		**59**				
Add, subtract, and multiply complex numbers		60				
Introduction to Imaginary and Complex Numbers		61				
Solving Quadratic Equations with Real Coefficients that have Complex Solutions		62				
Recognizing Reasonable Answers to Word Problems		63				
Evaluating Rational Exponents		64				
Simplifying Expressions with Rational Exponents		65				

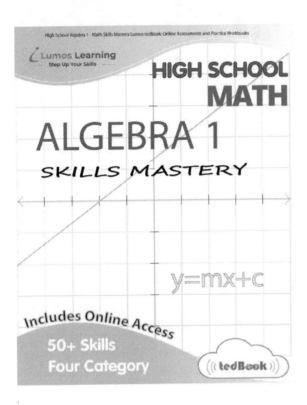

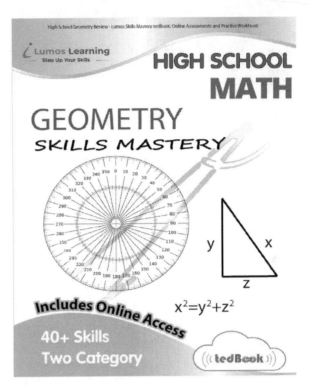

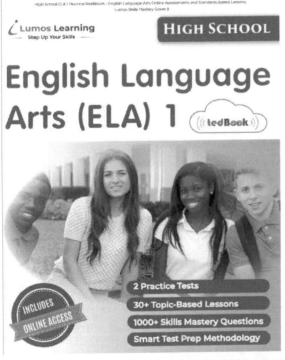

Made in the USA
Las Vegas, NV
28 February 2024